ADVANCED HIGHER CHEMISTRY

Calculations and Prescribed Practical Activities

David Calder

SCOTTISH
EXAMINATION
MATERIALS

HODDER
GIBSON
AN HACHETTE UK COMPANY

Every effort has been made to trace all copyright holders, but if any have been inadvertently overlooked the Publishers will be pleased to make the necessary arrangements at the first opportunity.

Although every effort has been made to ensure that website addresses are correct at time of going to press, Hodder Gibson cannot be held responsible for the content of any website mentioned in this book. It is sometimes possible to find a relocated web page by typing in the address of the home page for a website in the URL window of your browser.

Hachette's policy is to use papers that are natural, renewable and recyclable products and made from wood grown in sustainable forests. The logging and manufacturing processes are expected to conform to the environmental regulations of the country of origin.

Orders: please contact Bookpoint Ltd, 130 Park Drive, Abingdon, Oxon OX14 4SE. Telephone: (44) 01235 827720. Fax: (44) 01235 400454. Lines are open 9.00–5.00, Monday to Saturday, with a 24-hour message answering service. Visit our website at www.hoddereducation.co.uk. Hodder Gibson can be contacted direct on: Tel: 0141 848 1609; Fax: 0141 889 6315; email: hoddergibson@hodder.co.uk

© David Calder 2008
First published in 2008 by
Hodder Gibson, an imprint of Hodder Education,
an Hachette UK company
2a Christie Street
Paisley PA1 1NB

Impression number   7

Year   2014

Cover photo © Photodisc
Illustrations by DC Graphic Design, Swanley Village, Kent
Typeset in Sabon 11pt by DC Graphic Design, Swanley Village, Kent
Printed in Great Britain by CPI Group (UK) Ltd, Croydon, CR0 4YY

A catalogue record for this title is available from the British Library

ISBN-13: 978 0340 971 369

Contents

Note to Students and Teachers

Throughout the book it is expected that data is obtained from the Scottish Qualifications Authority Chemistry Data Book for Higher and Advanced Higher.

Answers are rounded to a maximum of three significant figures, except where a calculated value is, for example, exactly 2.345 where rounding up to 2.35 or down to 2.34 would be arbitrary. The answer 2.345 would be that given in the book.

Some calculations have several parts with separate answers which may be rounded as noted above. Depending on the extent to which answers are rounded during any such problem there may be a slight discrepancy between the final answer and that which would have been obtained had rounding taken place at each stage. Students should not be concerned about any *slight* difference between their answers and those given in the book in any such case.

In Unit 3 (Organic Chemistry) of the Advanced Higher syllabus, reference is made to only one type of calculation – the analysis of organic compounds by burning them and weighing the products formed. The involves methods very similar to those of the Gravimetric Analysis section of Unit 2. For this reason, calculations involving combustion analysis are specifically covered in Chapter 5 of this book.

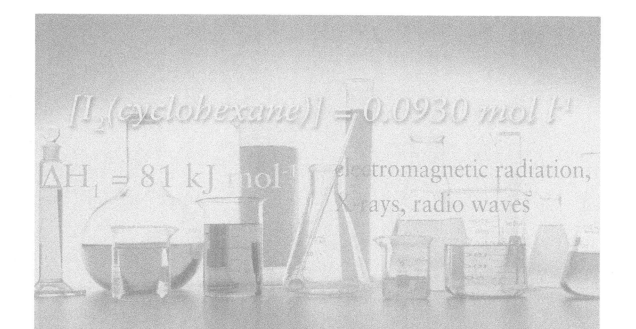

Part One
Calculations

Electromagnetic Radiation

The basic equation describing electromagnetic radiation, including light, X-rays, radio waves, etc., is:

$$c = \nu\lambda$$

where
c is the speed of light, 3×10^8 m s^{-1}
ν is the frequency of radiation, in s^{-1} (this unit is also known as Hertz, symbol Hz)
λ is the wavelength of radiation, in metres (m).

Note that ν is the Greek letter nu, not to be confused with the letter v in English. In some textbooks the more obvious symbol f for frequency is used. It is not wrong to use f, but you must also be able to recognise ν.

Looking at the equation, it can be seen that, since c is a **constant**, ν and λ are **inversely proportional**, i.e. as one quantity increases the other decreases.

A second relationship is shown by the equation below:

$$E = h\nu$$

where
E is the energy, in Joules (J)
h is the Planck Constant, 6.63×10^{-34} J s.

This means that the energy of radiation (E) is **directly proportional** to the frequency.

In the area of the visible spectrum, red is at the low-frequency / low-energy end; violet is at the high-frequency / high-energy end. Beyond these ends are invisible infra-red (IR) and ultra-violet (UV) areas. That the violet / UV end is high energy can be remembered by being aware of the fact that it is UV radiation from the Sun which causes sunburn and skin cancers.

The Planck Constant has a very small numerical value because it refers to **one photon of energy** being emitted or absorbed when one electron falls to a lower energy level or is promoted to a higher energy level. In chemistry we normally refer to energy changes involving **1 mole** of the substance.

This is shown in the equation below where L is the Avogadro Constant, 6.02×10^{23} mol⁻¹.

$$E = Lh\nu$$

The unit for E is now J mol⁻¹, and refers to the energy involved when 1 mole of photons is emitted or absorbed.

An alternative version of the above equation can be combined to relate the energy of radiation to its wavelength, as shown below.

$$E = \frac{Lhc}{\lambda}$$

Notes
1. Since the unit of h is J s, the unit of E is J. However, most problems will either give E in kJ mol⁻¹, or ask for E to be calculated in kJ mol⁻¹.

    The unit of λ is metres (m), but usually wavelength relating to electron transitions in atoms is given in nanometres (nm). 1 nm = 10^{-9} m.

    Energy must be in J and wavelength in m when using the equations.

2. The values for the Avogadro Constant, the Planck Constant and the speed of light are given on page 19 of the Data Book.

Worked Example 1.1

Calculate the energy, in kJ mol⁻¹, associated with the emissions causing a red line in the spectrum of a cadmium vapour lamp at a wavelength of 644 nm.

Answer
The equation below is selected and the data and constants inserted:

$$E = \frac{Lhc}{\lambda}$$

$$E = \frac{6.02 \times 10^{23} \times 6.63 \times 10^{-34} \times 3.00 \times 10^{8}}{644 \times 10^{-9}}$$

$$= 1.86 \times 10^5 \text{ J mol}^{-1}$$

$$= \textbf{186 kJ mol}^{-1}$$

Worked Example 1.2

Calculate the wavelength, in nm, of the light which would be required to break 1 mole of H–F bonds, using bond enthalpy data from page 9 of the Data Book.

Answer
From the Data Book, the bond enthalpy of H–F is 569 kJ mol^{-1}.

The appropriate equation connecting the wavelength of the light and the associated energy is selected.

$$E = \frac{Lhc}{\lambda}$$

This equation is rearranged to put the required quantity, λ, on the left-hand side.

$$\lambda = \frac{Lhc}{E}$$

The quantities involved are then put into the equation.

$$\lambda = \frac{6.02 \times 10^{23} \times 6.63 \times 10^{-34} \times 3.00 \times 10^8}{569 \times 10^3}$$

$$= 2.10 \times 10^{-7} \text{ m}$$

But the problem asks for the wavelength to be expressed in nm (nanometres); so the answer is

$$2.10 \times 10^{-7} \times 10^9 \text{ nm}$$

$$= \textbf{210 nm}$$

It is worth noting that this is the maximum wavelength which would break the H–F bonds, since a higher wavelength of light would have less energy which would not be enough to break the bonds. In practice, a lower wavelength, with higher energy, would be required.

PROBLEMS

1   Calculate the energy, in kJ mol^{-1}, of the electron transition that causes the orange–yellow spectral line in the helium spectrum with a wavelength of 706 nm.

2   When a barium compound is placed in a flame, a green flame appears, which has a prominent line in the spectrum.

(a) Refer to page 14 of the Data Book to obtain the wavelength of the electron transition causing this line.

(b) Calculate the energy, in kJ mol^{-1}, of the electron transition that causes this line.

3   Calculate the energy, in kJ mol^{-1}, of the electron transition that causes the line in the ultra-violet area of the hydrogen spectrum with a wavelength of 397 nm.

4   When a strontium compound is placed in a flame, a red colour appears, which has a prominent line in the spectrum.

(a) Refer to page 14 of the Data Book to obtain the wavelength of this line.

(b) Calculate the energy, in kJ mol^{-1}, of the electron transition related to this line.

5   Refer to page 14 of the Data Book.

(a) What is the wavelength of the electron transition causing an orange–yellow line in the helium spectrum?

(b) Calculate the energy, in kJ mol^{-1}, associated with this spectral line.

6   A line in the visible spectrum is caused by an electron transition with an associated energy of 193 kJ mol^{-1}. Calculate the wavelength of this line in nanometeres.

7   A line in the ultra-violet spectrum is caused by an electron transition with an associated energy of 308 kJ mol^{-1}. Calculate the wavelength of this line in nanometres.

8   A line in the visible spectrum is caused by an electron transition with an associated energy of 296 kJ mol^{-1}. Calculate the wavelength of this line in nanometres.

9   A line in the visible spectrum is caused by an electron transition with an associated energy of 246 kJ mol^{-1}. Calculate the wavelength of this line in nanometres.

10   When a metal compound is placed in a flame, a flame colour appears with a main spectral line with an associated energy of 368 kJ mol^{-1}. Calculate the wavelength of this line in nanometres.

Volumetric Analysis

Volumetric analysis is the determination of the concentration of one solution by titration with a solution of known concentration. This is essentially a revision of work done in earlier courses, but often with more complicated problems.

Worked Example 2.1

A solution of hydrochloric acid of unknown concentration was analysed by titration with standard sodium carbonate solution. A sample of anhydrous sodium carbonate was heated, and weighed at intervals, until no mass loss took place, to ensure that any water that might have been absorbed from the air was removed. This is known as 'heating to constant mass'. The dried sodium carbonate sample weighed 2.44 g. The sodium carbonate was dissolved and made up to 100 cm³ with distilled water in a standard flask.

10 cm³ portions of the hydrochloric acid were titrated with this sodium carbonate solution. The titres are given below.

Titre no.	Titre / cm³
1	22.3
2	21.4
3	21.3
4	21.5

The equation for the reaction taking place is:

$$Na_2CO_3(aq) + 2HCl(aq) \rightarrow 2NaCl(aq) + CO_2(g) + H_2O(l)$$

Calculate:

(a) the concentration of the standard sodium carbonate solution;

(b) the average titre of the sodium carbonate solution which should be used in this analysis;

(c)   the number of moles of sodium carbonate present in the average titre;

(d)   (from the balanced equation) the number of moles of hydrochloric acid which must have been present in a 10 cm³ sample;

(e)   the concentration of the acid.

Answer

(a)   The formula mass of Na_2CO_3 = 106.

The number of moles of sodium carbonate in the 2.44 g sample is 2.44 / 106 = 0.0230.

This number of moles of sodium carbonate is dissolved in 100 cm³. So the concentration of the sodium carbonate solution is **0.230 mol l⁻¹**.

(b)   The average titre is **21.4 cm³**. This is *not* the average of all the titres, but the average of those which are **concordant**, i.e. very close to each other. The first titre of 22.3 cm³ is ignored; the other three titres are close enough to be averaged for the calculation.

(c)   The concentration of the sodium carbonate solution is 0.230 mol l⁻¹ and the average titre is 21.4 cm³. So the number of moles of sodium carbonate is:

$$0.230 \times 0.0214 = \textbf{4.92} \times \textbf{10}^{-3}.$$

(d)   1 mol of Na_2CO_3 reacts with 2 mol of HCl.

So the number of moles of HCl = $2 \times 4.92 \times 10^{-3}$ = **9.84 × 10⁻³**.

(e)   The 9.84 × 10⁻³ mol of HCl is in a 10 cm³ sample. So the concentration of the acid is 9.84 × 10⁻³ / 0.01 = **0.984 mol l⁻¹**

PROBLEMS

1   A sample of sulphuric acid of unknown concentration is analysed by the following method. A 25 cm³ sample of the acid is dropped by pipette into a standard flask and made up to 250 cm³ with distilled water. Then 25 cm³ samples of this diluted solution were titrated with standard 0.10 mol l⁻¹ sodium hydroxide solution; the average titre was 33.5 cm³.

The equation for the reaction is given below.

$$H_2SO_4(aq) + 2NaOH(aq) \rightarrow Na_2SO_4(aq) + 2H_2O(l)$$

Calculate the concentration of the original sulphuric acid.

2   A bottle of vinegar was analysed to find the concentration of ethanoic acid it contained. A 25 cm³ sample of the vinegar was diluted to 250 cm³ in a standard flask; several 25 cm³ samples of the diluted vinegar were then titrated with standard 0.025 mol l⁻¹ sodium hydroxide solution. The average titre was 18.4 cm³. The reaction taking place in this titration is given below.

$$CH_3COOH(aq) + NaOH(aq) \rightarrow CH_3COONa(aq) + H_2O(l)$$

Calculate the concentration of the acid in the vinegar, assuming that ethanoic acid is the only acid present.

3   A nickel(II) sulphate solution was analysed by titration with ethylenediaminetetraacetic acid (EDTA) solution with an appropriate indicator. EDTA forms a complex with Ni^{2+} on a 1 : 1 molar basis. A 10 cm³ sample of the nickel(II) sulphate solution was dropped by pipette into a 100 cm³ standard flask and made up to the mark with distilled water. Several 10 cm³ samples of the diluted solution were titrated with standard 0.01 mol l⁻¹ EDTA solution; the results are shown in the table below.

Titre no.	Titre / cm³
1	14.3
2	14.1
3	14.9
4	14.2

(a) Calculate the average titre which should be used in this analysis.

(b) Calculate the concentration of the original nickel(II) sulphate solution.

4 A 3.64 g sample of impure phthalic acid, $C_6H_4(COOH)_2$, was analysed by titration with standard 0.10 mol l^{-1} sodium hydroxide solution. The sample was dissolved in distilled water and made up to 250 cm^3 in a standard flask. Then 25 cm^3 samples of this diluted solution were titrated with the sodium hydroxide solution; the average titre was 34.8 cm^3.

The equation for the neutralisation taking place in the titration is:

$$C_6H_4(COOH)_2(aq) + 2NaOH(aq) \rightarrow C_6H_4(COONa)_2(aq) + 2H_2O(l)$$

Assuming that the only reaction taking place in the analysis is that given by the above equation, calculate:

(a) the mass of pure phthalic acid present in the original sample;

(b) the percentage, by mass, of pure phthalic acid in the original sample.

5 A bottle of hydrochloric acid of unknown concentration was analysed as follows.

Anhydrous sodium carbonate, Na_2CO_3, was heated to constant mass (to make sure that any water which might have been present was removed). A 2.43 g sample of the dried substance was dissolved and made up to 250 cm^3 with distilled water in a standard flask. Then 10 cm^3 portions of the hydrochloric acid were titrated against the sodium carbonate solution using a suitable indicator to determine the endpoint. The average titre of the sodium carbonate solution was 22.3 cm^3.

The equation for the neutralisation is:

$$Na_2CO_3(aq) + 2HCl(aq) \rightarrow 2NaCl(aq) + CO_2(g) + H_2O(l)$$

Calculate:

(a) the concentration of the sodium carbonate solution;

(b) the concentration of the hydrochloric acid.

6 'Hard water' in the water supply is water which contains ions, including $Ca^{2+}(aq)$. Hard water makes it difficult to obtain a lather using soap and can cause damaging deposits on the inside of water pipes and appliances.

A sample of hard water was analysed by titration with ethylenediaminetetraacetic acid (EDTA) using an indicator specific to calcium ions. EDTA forms a complex on a 1 : 1 molar basis with $Ca^{2+}(aq)$. 10 cm³ of the hard water was diluted to 100 cm³ and several 10 cm³ samples of this diluted solution were titrated with standard 0.010 mol l⁻¹ EDTA solution. The average titre was 24.9 cm³.

Calculate the concentration of calcium ions in the original water sample.

7 The concentration of a potassium hydroxide solution was determined as follows. A 25 cm³ sample of the potassium hydroxide solution was made up to 250 cm³ solution in a standard flask. Then 2.47 g of pure oxalic acid, $(COOH)_2$, was dissolved in distilled water to make up a 250 cm³ standard solution. Several 25 cm³ samples of the diluted potassium hydroxide solution were titrated with the standard oxalic acid solution. The average titre of the acid solution was 17.9 cm³. The equation for the neutralisation taking place is:

$$(COOH)_2(aq) + 2KOH(aq) \rightarrow (COOK)_2(aq) + 2H_2O(l)$$

Calculate the concentration of the original potassium hydroxide solution.

8 The concentration of a solution of malonic acid, $CH_2(COOH)_2$, was measured by titration against a standard 0.05 mol l⁻¹ solution of sodium hydroxide. A 25 cm³ sample of the acid solution was made up to 250 cm³ with distilled water in a standard flask. Then 25 cm³ samples of this diluted solution were titrated with the sodium hydroxide solution. The average titre was 12.6 cm³.

The equation for the neutralisation taking place is:

$$CH_2(COOH)_2(aq) + 2NaOH(aq) \rightarrow CH_2(COONa)_2(aq) + 2H_2O(l)$$

Calculate the concentration of the original malonic acid solution.

9 A phosphoric acid solution was analysed by titration with standard 0.01 mol l⁻¹ sodium hydroxide solution. The equation for the neutralisation involved is given below.

$$H_3PO_4(aq) + 3NaOH(aq) \rightarrow Na_3PO_4(aq) + 3H_2O(l)$$

10 cm^3 of the acid solution was made up to 100 cm^3 in a standard flask. Several 10 cm^3 samples of this diluted solution were titrated with the sodium hydroxide solution. The average titre was 17.9 cm^3. Calculate the concentration of the original phosphoric acid solution.

10   A container of impure zinc sulphate, $ZnSO_4$, was analysed using ethylenediaminetetraacetic acid (EDTA) using an indicator specific to zinc(II) ions. The Zn^{2+}(aq) reacts on a 1 : 1 mole ratio with EDTA. A 6.72 g sample of the impure zinc(II) sulphate was dissolved in distilled water, filtered to remove any insoluble substances, and the remaining solution made up to 250 cm^3 in a standard flask. Several 25 cm^3 samples of this solution were titrated with standard 0.10 mol l^{-1} EDTA solution. The average titre was 22.3 cm^3.

(a) Calculate the mass of $ZnSO_4$ in the sample taken from the container.

(b) Express this is a percentage, by mass, of the original container sample.

Redox Titrations

Redox reactions can often be used to obtain the concentration of an unknown solution by titration. In the process one solution is reduced and the other is oxidised. In some cases the endpoint of the titration is detected by one of the substances changing colour; such titrations are referred to as being self-indicating. In other cases an indicator is required. This chapter is mainly an important revision of Higher work.

Worked Example 3.1

The ion-electron equations for the redox reaction between permanganate ions, $MnO_4^-(aq)$, in acid solution and sulphite ions, $SO_3^{2-}(aq)$, are given below. Note that the permanganate ion is also known more systematically as manganate (VII), although the former term is more commonly used and will be used in this book. Students should, however, be able to recognise the latter term.

$$MnO_4^-(aq) + 8H^+(aq) + 5e^- \rightarrow Mn^{2+}(aq) + 4H_2O(l)$$

$$SO_3^{2-}(aq) + H_2O(l) \rightarrow SO_4^{2-}(aq) + 2H^+(aq) + 2e^-$$

50 cm³ of standard 0.02 mol l⁻¹ acidified potassium permanganate solution was titrated with a sulphite ion solution of unknown concentration. It took 17.3 cm³ of the sulphite solution to turn the permanganate solution from purple to clear. Calculate the concentration of the sulphite solution.

Answer
We start by noting that the reduction of 1 mol of the $MnO_4^-(aq)$ requires 5 mol of electrons, and the oxidation of 1 mol of $SO_3^{2-}(aq)$ produces 2 mol of electrons. In order to balance the electrons we multiply the ion-electron equations as below.

$$2 \times [MnO_4^-(aq) + 8H^+(aq) + 5e^- \rightarrow Mn^{2+}(aq) + 4H_2O(l)]$$

$$5 \times [SO_3^{2-}(aq) + H_2O(l) \rightarrow SO_4^{2-}(aq) + 2H^+(aq) + 2e^-]$$

There is no need to carry out these multiplications and then work out the full balanced equation for the overall redox reaction. We simply note that 2 mol of $MnO_4^-(aq)$ is gaining 10 mol of electrons and 5 mol of SO_3^{2-}(aq) is losing 10 mol of electrons. Since the electrons are now balanced we can say that:

$$2 \text{ mol of } MnO_4^-\text{(aq) reacts with 5 mol of } SO_3^{2-}\text{(aq)}$$

This gives us the mole statement on which to base the calculation.

We know the volume and concentration of the MnO_4^-(aq) so we can calculate the number of moles.

$$0.05 \times 0.02 = 0.001 \text{ mol of } MnO_4^-\text{(aq)}$$

We then use this to calculate the number of moles of the SO_3^{2-}(aq).

2 mol of MnO_4^-(aq) reacts with 5 mol of SO_3^{2-}(aq)
1 mol of MnO_4^-(aq) reacts with 2.5 mol of SO_3^{2-}(aq)
0.001 mol of MnO_4^-(aq) reacts with 0.001×2.5 mol of SO_3^{2-}(aq)
= 0.0025 mol of SO_3^{2-}(aq)

We know that the volume of the SO_3^{2-}(aq) solution is 17.3 cm³ = 0.0173 litres. So the concentration of the SO_3^{2-}(aq) solution is

$$0.0025 / 0.0173$$

$$= 0.145 \text{ mol l}^{-1}$$

Worked Example 3.2

50 cm³ of a 0.15 mol l⁻¹ solution of potassium iodide was treated with an excess of an oxidising agent to convert all the I⁻(aq) ions to I_2(aq) according to the oxidation below.

$$2I^-\text{(aq)} \rightarrow I_2\text{(aq)} + 2e^-$$

The I_2(aq) formed was titrated with sodium thiosulphate solution, $Na_2S_2O_3$(aq), using starch as the indicator. The reactions taking place in this titration are:

$$I_2\text{(aq)} + 2e^- \rightarrow 2I^-\text{(aq)}$$

$$2S_2O_3^{2-}\text{(aq)} \rightarrow S_4O_6^{2-}\text{(aq)} + 2e^-$$

The endpoint was at 25.0 cm³ of $S_2O_3^{2-}$(aq).

(a) Calculate the number of moles of $I^-(aq)$ in the original solution.

(b) Calculate the number of moles of $I_2(aq)$ formed after the $I^-(aq)$ was treated with the oxidising agent.

(c) Calculate the number of moles of $S_2O_3{}^{2-}(aq)$ which would have reacted in the titration of the $I_2(aq)$ calculated in (b) above.

(d) Calculate the concentration of the original sodium thiosulphate solution.

Answer

(a) The volume is 0.05 litres and the concentration is 0.15 mol l^{-1}, so the number of moles of $I^-(aq)$ is $0.05 \times 0.15 =$ **0.0075 mol.**

(b) From the ion-electron equation given, 2 mol of $I^-(aq)$ forms 1 mol of $I_2(aq)$. So the number of moles of $I_2(aq) = 0.0075 / 2 =$ **0.00375 mol.**

(c) The electrons in the reduction and oxidation equations given are already balanced, with 2e$^-$ in each equation. So we can say that:

$$1 \text{ mol of } I_2(aq) \text{ reacts with 2 mol of } S_2O_3{}^{2-}(aq)$$

$$0.00375 \text{ mol of } I_2(aq) \text{ reacts with } 2 \times 0.00375 \text{ mol of } S_2O_3{}^{2-}(aq)$$

Therefore the number of moles of $S_2O_3{}^{2-}(aq)$ is **0.0075 mol.**

(d) Concentration $= 0.0075 / 0.025 =$ **0.30 mol l^{-1}.**

PROBLEMS

1 The ion-electron equations below show the reduction and oxidation reactions taking place when a solution of acidified dichromate ions is reacted with a solution of sulphite ions.

$$Cr_2O_7{}^{2-}(aq) + 14H^+(aq) + 6e^- \rightarrow 2Cr^{3+}(aq) + 7H_2O(l)$$

$$SO_3{}^{2-}(aq) + H_2O(l) \rightarrow SO_4{}^{2-}(aq) + 2H^+(aq) + 2e^-$$

What volume of a 0.05 mol l^{-1} solution of dichromate ions would react with 30 cm^3 of a 0.25 mol l^{-1} solution of sulphite ions?

2 Consider the ion-electron equations below which describe the redox reaction between permanganate ions, MnO_4^-, in acid solution (to provide the necessary $H^+(aq)$ for the reduction), and chloride ions.

$$MnO_4^-(aq) + 8H^+(aq) + 5e^- \rightarrow Mn^{2+}(aq) + 4H_2O(l)$$

$$2Cl^-(aq) \rightarrow Cl_2(g) + 2e^-$$

What volume of a 0.24 mol l^{-1} solution of acidified permanganate ions would react with 120 cm^3 of a 0.16 mol l^{-1} solution of chloride ions?

3 A 25 cm^3 sample of sodium bromate solution, $NaBrO_3$, was diluted to 250 cm^3 in a standard flask. 25 cm^3 samples of this diluted solution were titrated with 0.80 mol l^{-1} sodium iodide solution using a starch indicator. The reduction and oxidation reactions taking place were:

$$2BrO_3^-(aq) + 12H^+(aq) + 10e^- \rightarrow Br_2(aq) + 6H_2O(l)$$

$$2I^-(aq) \rightarrow I_2(aq) + 2e^-$$

The volumes of the sodium iodide solution titres are given below.

Titre no.	Titre / cm³
1	34.2
2	33.7
3	33.6
4	33.5

(a) Which value should be taken for the average titre in the calculation?

(b) Calculate the average number of moles of iodide ions in a 25 cm^3 titre.

(c) Calculate the concentration of the original sodium bromate solution.

4 A 2.49 g steel bolt was analysed to find the percentage of iron it contained. The bolt was dissolved in an excess of dilute sulphuric acid converting all the iron present to iron(II) ions according to the equation below.

$$Fe(s) \rightarrow Fe^{2+}(aq) + 2e^-$$

The solution was made up to 250 cm³ with distilled water in a standard flask. Several 25 cm³ samples of this solution were titrated with standard 0.05 mol l⁻¹ acidified potassium permanganate solution.

The only reactions taking place in this titration were:

$$Fe^{2+}(aq) \rightarrow Fe^{3+}(aq) + e^-$$

$$MnO_4^-(aq) + 8H^+(aq) + 5e^- \rightarrow Mn^{2+}(aq) + 4H_2O(l)$$

The average titre of the permanganate solution was found to be 16.4 cm³.

(a) Calculate the number of moles of the potassium permanganate solution present in an average titre.

(b) Calculate the number of moles of $Fe^{2+}(aq)$ in an average 25 cm³ sample.

(c) Calculate the mass of iron in the bolt.

(d) Express this mass as a percentage of the iron in the steel.

5 A 5.82 g sample of impure ethanedioic acid, $(COOH)_2$, is dissolved in distilled water and made up to 250 cm³ in a standard flask. Then 25 cm³ portions of this solution are titrated against standard 0.10 mol l⁻¹ acidified potassium permanganate. The only reactions taking place are:

$$MnO_4^-(aq) + 8H^+(aq) + 5e^- \rightarrow Mn^{2+}(aq) + 4H_2O(l)$$

$$(COOH)_2 \rightarrow 2CO_2(g) + 2H^+(aq) + 2e^-$$

It took an average titre of 24.2 cm³ to reach the endpoint in the titration.

Calculate the percentage purity, by mass, of the original ethanedioic acid sample.

6 The active ingredient in bleaches is the hypochlorite ion, OCl^-. The concentration of this ion in a bleach can be analysed as follows. The bleach is treated with an excess of potassium iodide solution. This causes a redox reaction, the overall equation for which is:

$$OCl^-(aq) + 2H^+(aq) + 2I^-(aq) \rightarrow I_2(aq) + Cl^-(aq) + H_2O(l)$$

The quantity of iodine formed in this reaction can be measured by titrating with standard sodium thiosulphate solution, $Na_2S_2O_3(aq)$. The oxidation and reduction reactions taking place are:

$$2S_2O_3{}^{2-}(aq) \rightarrow S_4O_6{}^{2-}(aq) + 2e^-$$

$$I_2(aq) + 2e^- \rightarrow 2I^-(aq)$$

To find the concentration of hypochlorite ion in a bleach, a 10 cm³ sample of bleach was treated with an excess of potassium iodide solution and diluted to 250 cm³ in a standard flask. Several 25 cm³ samples were titrated with 0.10 mol l⁻¹ sodium thiosulphate solution using starch as an indicator. The average titre was 12.4 cm³.

(a) Calculate the number of moles of hypochlorite ions in 25.0 cm³ of the diluted bleach.

(b) Calculate the concentration of hypochlorite ions in the original bleach.

7   A sample of steel weighing 1.43 g was analysed to find the percentage of iron present. The steel was dissolved completely in an excess of dilute sulphuric acid, during which all the iron was converted to iron(II) ions, $Fe^{2+}(aq)$. The solution was made up to 250 cm³ with more dilute sulphuric acid in a standard flask. Then 25 cm³ portions of this solution were titrated with standard 0.02 mol l⁻¹ potassium dichromate solution. The only reactions taking place were:

$$Fe^{2+}(aq) \rightarrow Fe^{3+}(aq) + e^-$$

$$Cr_2O_7{}^{2-}(aq) + 14H^+(aq) + 6e^- \rightarrow 2Cr^{3+}(aq) + 7H_2O(l)$$

The titre results are given below

Titre no.	Titre / cm³
1	21.3
2	18.6
3	18.5
4	18.7

(a) Calculate the average titre which should be used in this calculation.

(b) Calculate the number of moles of $Fe^{2+}(aq)$ in the average 25 cm^3 sample.

(c) Calculate the number of moles of $Fe^{2+}(aq)$ in the 250 cm^3 solution.

(d) Calculate the mass of iron in the original sample of steel.

(e) Express the mass of iron as a percentage of the original sample.

8 A bottle of sodium iodate solution, $NaIO_3$, of unknown concentration, is analysed by the following procedure. A 25 cm^3 sample of the solution was diluted to 250 cm^3 with distilled water in a standard flask. Several 25 cm^3 samples of this diluted solution were treated with an excess of a reducing agent to convert all the iodate ions present to iodine, I_2. The reduction taking place is shown below.

$$2IO_3^-(aq) \ + \ 12H^+(aq) \ + \ 10e^- \ \rightarrow \ I_2(aq) \ + \ 6H_2O(l)$$

The iodine produced in this reaction was titrated with a standard solution of 0.10 mol l^{-1} sodium thiosulphate, $Na_2S_2O_3$. A starch indicator was used to determine the endpoint of the titration. The reduction and oxidation reactions taking place were:

$$I_2(aq) \ + \ 2e^- \ \rightarrow \ 2I^-(aq)$$

$$2S_2O_3^{2-}(aq) \ \rightarrow \ S_4O_6^{2-}(aq) \ + \ 2e^-$$

The average titre of the sodium thiosulphate solution was 31.2 cm^3. Calculate:

(a) the number of moles of the sodium thiosulphate solution in the average titre;

(b) the number of moles of iodine which were in the 250 cm^3 standard flask;

(c) the concentration of sodium iodate ion in the original bottle.

9 A bottle of hydrogen peroxide solution, $H_2O_2(aq)$, was analysed by reacting as follows.

A 25 cm^3 sample of the solution was diluted to 250 cm^3 in a standard flask. Several 25 cm^3 samples of the diluted solution were titrated with standard 0.02 mol l^{-1} acidified potassium dichromate solution.

The reduction and oxidation reactions taking place in the titration were:

$$Cr_2O_7^{2-}(aq) + 14H^+(aq) + 6e^- \rightarrow 2Cr^{3+}(aq) + 7H_2O(l)$$

$$H_2O_2(aq) \rightarrow O_2(g) + 2H^+(aq) + 2e^-$$

The endpoint of this titration is observed when the orange colour of the dichromate changes to the green of the chromium(III) ion. The average titre of the dichromate solution was 35.8 cm^3.

(a) Calculate the number of moles of hydrogen peroxide in the average 25 cm^3 diluted sample.

(b) Calculate the number of moles of hydrogen peroxide in the 25 cm^3 sample which was taken from the original bottle.

(c) Calculate the concentration of the hydrogen peroxide solution in the original bottle.

10 A sample of processed food was analysed for chloride ions to assess the content of sodium chloride present. The analysis was carried out by redox titration with acidified potassium permanganate solution. The reduction and oxidation reactions were:

$$MnO_4^-(aq) + 8H^+(aq) + 5e^- \rightarrow Mn^{2+}(aq) + 4H_2O(l)$$

$$2Cl^-(aq) \rightarrow Cl_2(aq) + 2e^-$$

32.4 g of the food was liquidised in a food mixer, filtered, and the solution made up to 500 cm^3 in a standard flask. Then 25 cm^3 portions of this solution were extracted by pipette and titrated against standard 0.02 mol l^{-1} acidified potassium permanganate solution. The average titre was 23.6 cm^3.

(a) Calculate the number of moles of chloride present in the average 25 cm^3 sample, assuming that the above equations represent the only reactions taking place.

(b) Calculate the mass of sodium chloride in the original food sample, assuming that sodium chloride is the only source of the chloride present.

(c) Express this mass as a percentage of the mass of sodium chloride in the original food sample.

Empirical Formulae

The term **empirical** means 'obtained by experiment'. Empirical formulae are those calculated by analysing substances experimentally to calculate the masses of the different elements they contain.

Worked Example 4.1

A sample of an oxide of copper is analysed and found to contain 2.54 g of copper combined with 0.32 g of oxygen. Calculate the empirical formula of the compound.

Answer
The first step is to put the information into a table as below, including the mole masses of the elements.

Element:	Cu	O
Actual mass:	2.54 g	0.32 g
Mass of 1 mol:	63.5 g	16.0 g

We now calculate how many moles of each element are present in the compound by dividing the actual masses by the mole masses.

	Cu	O
Actual moles:	$\dfrac{2.54}{63.5}$	$\dfrac{0.32}{16.0}$
	$= 0.04$	$= 0.02$

What we are looking for is the **simplest whole number ratio** connecting these actual mole values. Just by looking at the numbers it should be obvious that the ratio is as below.

Whole number ratio:	2	1

This means that there are two Cu for every one O in the formula. **So the empirical formula is Cu_2O.**

Worked Example 4.2

A sample of chromium oxide contains 68.4% chromium by mass. Calculate the empirical formula of the compound.

Answer

In this example, the proportion of each element is expressed as a percentage mass. The easiest way to handle this is to imagine that we have a 100 g sample of the element. So the 'sample' contains 68.4 g of chromium. Since the only other element is oxygen, its mass must be 31.6 g. The problem is set out as in Worked Example 4.1.

Element:	Cr	O
Actual mass:	68.4 g	31.6 g
Mass of 1 mol:	52.0 g	16.0 g
Actual moles:	$\dfrac{68.4}{52}$	$\dfrac{31.6}{16}$
	= 1.315*	= 1.975

* rounded value

This is the ratio of chromium and oxygen particles in the compound. However, the **whole number ratio** is not obvious as in the previous Worked Example. In a situation like this, the best way to deal with it is to **divide both numbers by the smaller.**

Ratio:	$\dfrac{1.315}{1.315}$	$\dfrac{1.975}{1.315}$
	= 1	= 1.5*

* rounded value

The purpose of this was to make the smaller of the numbers in the ratio equal to 1. We still do not have a whole number for the oxygen, but it should be obvious that if we **multiply both values by 2**, we get the whole number ratio below.

Whole number ratio:	2	3

The empirical formula of the compound is therefore Cr_2O_3.

Note

Before leaving this Worked Example, it should be noted that at two points in this calculation (indicated by *) numbers were rounded from the values obtained on a calculator. Why do the numbers not work out to be *exactly* the simple numbers we are looking for?

One reason is that the original values came from experiments, and there will always be a certain amount of error there. Also the percentage masses given in the problem might have been rounded. For example, the percentage of chromium might have been rounded from 68.412% to 68.4%, perhaps because the original experimental measurements might not justify that level of accuracy.

A point of advice is not to round numbers too much until the final part of the calculation. For example, in this problem, the original value for the proportion of chromium was 68.4%. At the 'actual moles' stage in the calculation, it was reasonable to round the chromium value to 1.315 from the calculator value of 1.31538 etc., but rounding to 1 or 1.3 would be introducing unwanted error in the problem which could make the final whole number ratio difficult to see.

PROBLEMS

1   A sample of tin oxide contains 2.38 g of tin combined with 0.640 g of oxygen. Calculate the empirical formula of the compound.

2   A hydrocarbon contains 75% carbon by mass. Calculate the empirical formula of the compound.

3   A 2.30 g sample of an oxide of nitrogen is found to contain 0.70 g of nitrogen.

Calculate:

(a) the empirical formula of the nitrogen oxide;

(b) the molecular formula of the nitrogen oxide, given that its molecular mass is 92.

4   A sample of a hydrocarbon is analysed and found to contain approximately 85.7% of carbon by mass.

Calculate:

(a) the empirical formula of the hydrocarbon;

(b) the molecular formula of the hydrocarbon, given that its molecular mass is 140.

5   A 6.12 g sample of a compound of silicon and hydrogen, known as a silane, is analysed and found to contain 0.50 g of hydrogen. The molecular mass of the compound is known to be 122.4.

Calculate:

(a) the empirical formula of the compound;

(b) the molecular formula of the compound.

6   A sample of an organic nitrogen compound is analysed and found to contain 2.10 g of carbon, 2.45 g of nitrogen and 0.70 g of hydrogen. The molecular mass of the compound is known to be 60.

Calculate:

(a) the empirical formula of the compound;

(b) the formula of the compound.

7   The composition, by mass, of a compound is found to be calcium (38.7%), phosphorus (20%) and oxygen (41.3%). Calculate the empirical formula of the compound.

8   A compound of iron is found to have the following approximate composition by mass: iron (28.5%), carbon (30.6%), oxygen (40.9%). Calculate the empirical formula of the compound.

9   A sample of a compound containing barium, sulphur and oxygen is found to have the following composition by mass: barium (63.1%), sulphur (14.8%), oxygen (22.1%). Calculate the empirical formula of the compound.

10   A compound contains, by mass, approximately 21.8% carbon, 1.2% hydrogen and 77.0% iodine.

Calculate:

(a) the empirical formula of the compound;

(b) the molecular formula of the compound given that its molecular mass is 329.8.

Gravimetric Analysis

Gravimetric analysis means analysis of substances by weighing. Calculations on this topic usually do not require any theory beyond that of Higher, with the exception of problems involving empirical formulae, which some students may not have come across before. All students are advised to work through the previous topic in this book first.

Worked Example 5.1

An impure sample of aluminium sulphate was analysed by the following method. A sample of the substance weighing 5.42 g was dissolved in water and filtered to remove any insoluble material. The solution was treated with an excess of sodium hydroxide solution, causing a precipitate of aluminium hydroxide to be formed. The equation for this reaction is:

$$Al_2(SO_4)_3(aq) + 6NaOH(aq) \rightarrow 2Al(OH)_3(s) + 3Na_2SO_4(aq)$$

The precipitate of aluminium hydroxide was filtered, washed to remove any soluble substances, dried and weighed. The mass of the precipitate was 2.07 g.

Assuming that the only substance in the precipitate is aluminium hydroxide, calculate:

(a) the number of moles of aluminium hydroxide in the precipitate;

(b) (from the equation above) the number of moles of aluminium sulphate in the original sample;

(c) the mass of aluminium sulphate in the original sample;

(d) the percentage purity (by mass) of aluminium sulphate in the original sample.

Answer

(a) 1 mol of $Al(OH)_3$ = 78 g so the precipitate of 2.07 g = **0.0265 mol.**

(b) From the balanced equation:

1 mol of $Al_2(SO_4)_3$ reacts to form 2 mol of $Al(OH)_3$

So the number of moles of aluminium sulphate is 0.0265 / 2 = **0.01325**.

(c) 1 mole of $Al_2(SO_4)_3$ = 342.3 g

So 0.01325 mol = 0.01325 × 342.3 = **4.54 g**

(d) 4.54 g of $Al_2(SO_4)_3$ present in the 5.42 g sample = **83.8%**.

Worked Example 5.2

Copper(II) sulphate can exist in a white anhydrous ('without water') form, $CuSO_4$, and a blue hydrated form, $CuSO_4.xH_2O$. In the hydrated form a number of water molecules, designated x in the formula, are associated with each $CuSO_4$ in the formula. These water molecules are not strongly attached and can be removed by heating.

A 6.24 g sample of hydrated copper(II) sulphate was heated until the blue colour of the hydrated compound was replaced by the white of the anhydrous substance. To confirm that all the 'water of crystallisation' had been removed, the heated sample was weighed and re-heated several times until no more loss of mass was detected. (This is known as 'heating to constant mass'.) The remaining anhydrous copper(II) sulphate weighed 3.99 g.

Calculate the value of x in the formula $CuSO_4.xH_2O$.

Answer
The method for doing this calculation is very similar to that for calculating empirical formula (see Chapter 4). What we need to find is the mole ratio of $CuSO_4$: H_2O, that is, how many moles of water are present in the hydrated compound for every mole of $CuSO_4$.

The steps involved are to:

(a) obtain the mass of water present in the sample of the hydrated compound;

(b) calculate the number of moles of $CuSO_4$ and H_2O in the sample of the hydrated compound;

(c) express the mole ratio of the number of moles of H_2O associated with 1 mol of $CuSO_4$ in the hydrated compound.

The mass of water present in the hydrated sample is obtained by subtracting the mass of the anhydrous compound, i.e. 6.24 g – 3.99 g = **2.25 g of water**.

We set out the information in the form of a table (as in the empirical formula calculations in Chapter 4).

	$CuSO_4$	H_2O
Mass:	3.99 g	2.25 g
Mass of 1 mol:	159.6 g	18.0 g
Number of moles:	0.025	0.125

Dividing both numbers of moles by the smaller (0.025), we have:

Mole ratio:	1	5

So the value of x is 5 and the formula of the hydrated compound is therefore $CuSO_4.5H_2O$.

Worked Example 5.3

An organic liquid containing only carbon, hydrogen and oxygen was analysed by burning a sample and collecting the products using the apparatus below. The burner and contents, and the containers collecting water and carbon dioxide were weighed before and after a period of burning.

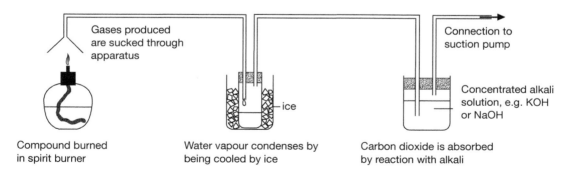

Gases produced are sucked through apparatus

Connection to suction pump

ice

Concentrated alkali solution, e.g. KOH or NaOH

Compound burned in spirit burner

Water vapour condenses by being cooled by ice

Carbon dioxide is absorbed by reaction with alkali

In this analysis, 2.73 g of the compound burned to produce 3.96 g of carbon dioxide and 1.89 g of water.

Calculate:

(a) the masses of carbon, hydrogen and oxygen present in the compound;

(b) the number of moles of carbon, hydrogen and oxygen present;

(c) the empirical formula of the compound.

Answer

(a) All the carbon from the burned compound is in the carbon dioxide formed so the mass of carbon in the compound is:

$$\frac{12}{44} \times 3.96 = \textbf{1.08 g}$$

All the hydrogen from the burned compound is in the water formed so the mass of hydrogen is:

$$\frac{2}{18} \times 1.89 = \textbf{0.21 g}$$

We are told that the compound contains only carbon, hydrogen and oxygen and that its mass is 2.73 g. So the mass of oxygen must be 2.73 minus the combined masses of carbon and hydrogen: that is,

$$2.73 - (1.08 + 0.21) = \textbf{1.44 g}$$

(b) The number of moles of carbon present in the compound is:

$$\frac{1.08}{12} = \textbf{0.09 mol}$$

The number of moles of hydrogen present is:

$$\frac{0.21}{1} = \textbf{0.21 mol}$$

The number of moles of oxygen present is:

$$\frac{1.44}{16} = \textbf{0.09 mol}$$

(c)   We set out a table as follows and work out the whole number ratio of the atoms in the compound. (Refer to Chapter 4: Empirical Formulae if this is unfamiliar.)

Element:	C	H	O
Number of moles:	0.09	0.21	0.09

Dividing each of the above values by the smallest (0.09) we have:

Mole ratio:	1	2.333	1

The repeating .333 is $\frac{1}{3}$, so 2.333 is $2\frac{1}{3}$. We can then get the whole number ratio by multiplying all the values by 3 to get:

Whole number ratio:	3	7	3

So the empirical formula of the compound is $C_3H_7O_3$.

PROBLEMS

1   A 5.02 g sample of an alloy containing silver was analysed as follows. The sample was dissolved completely in excess dilute nitric acid. The solution was then treated with an excess of sodium chloride solution, causing a precipitate of silver chloride, AgCl, to be formed. No other substance was precipitated. The precipitate was filtered, washed and dried. The precipitate weighed 2.37 g.

(a)   Calculate the mass of silver in the alloy.

(b)   Express this mass as a percentage of the alloy.

2   A 6.32 g nail consisting mainly of iron was dissolved in an excess of dilute hydrochloric acid, causing all the iron present to be converted to iron(II) chloride solution. After removal of all other substances the iron(II) chloride solution was evaporated to dryness, leaving 11.4 g of solid.

(a)   Calculate the mass of iron present in the nail.

(b)   Express this mass as a percentage of the mass of the nail.

3   A sample of anhydrous sodium sulphite, Na_2SO_3, contains sodium sulphate, Na_2SO_4, as the only impurity. 6.35 g of the sample was dissolved in distilled water and an excess of barium chloride solution was added. This resulted in a precipitate of a mixture of barium sulphite, $BaSO_3$, and barium sulphate, $BaSO_4$. This precipitate was treated with an excess of dilute hydrochloric acid which dissoved the barium sulphite but not the barium sulphate. The solid barium sulphate was filtered, dried and weighed; its mass was found to be 1.67 g.

Calculate:

(a) the number of moles of barium sulphate in the precipitate;

(b) the mass of sodium sulphate in the original sample;

(c) the mass of sodium sulphite in the original sample;

(d) the percentage, by mass, of sodium sulphite in the original sample.

4 A food is analysed for the presence of sodium chloride. A sample of the food weighing 152.4 g was liquidised with added water to dissolve all the soluble substances present. The food/water mixture was filtered and the filtrate treated with an excess of silver nitrate solution causing a precipitate of silver chloride, AgCl, weighing 3.02 g to be formed. No other product was present in the precipitate.

(a) Assuming that sodium chloride is the only source of chloride ions in the food, calculate the mass of sodium chloride in the sample.

(b) What is the percentage by mass of sodium chloride in the food?

5 An alloy containing lead was analysed as follows. A 7.34 g sample was dissolved completely in excess dilute nitric acid. The solution was then treated with an excess of sodium sulphate solution causing a precipitate of lead(II) sulphate, $PbSO_4$, to be formed. No other product is present in the precipitate. The precipitate was washed, dried and weighed; its mass was 7.48 g.

(a) Calculate the mass of lead present in the alloy.

(b) Express this mass as a percentage of lead in the alloy.

6 A 2.50 g sample of hydrated sodium phosphate, formula $Na_3PO_4.xH_2O$, where x represents a whole number, was heated until no further mass loss took place. The remaining anhydrous salt weighed 2.05 g.

Calculate:

(a) the number of moles of the anhydrous salt present;

(b) the number of moles of water present in the original, hydrated, salt sample;

(c) the value of x, that is the number of moles of water present in the hydrated sample for every mole of salt, using the answers to (a) and (b) above.

7   A 0.966 g sample of hydrated copper(II) nitrate was heated to constant mass, leaving 0.750 g of the anhydrous salt, $Cu(NO_3)_2$.

(a) How many moles of water were present in the original hydrated sample for every mole of the anhydrous compound?

(b) Write the full formula for the hydrated compound.

8   'Washing soda' is an old term used to describe hydrated sodium carbonate, $Na_2CO_3.xH_2O$. A 12.14 g sample of washing soda was heated until no further mass loss took place. The remaining anhydrous sodium carbonate weighed 4.50 g.

(a) Calculate the value of x in the formula for washing soda.

(b) Write the full formula for the hydrated compound.

9   An 10.40 g sample of hydrated iron(II) sulphate was heated until constant mass, leaving 6.08 g of the anhydrous salt, $FeSO_4$.

(a) Calculate the number of moles of water present for every mole of $FeSO_4$ present in the hydrated compound.

(b) Obtain the formula of the hydrated compound.

10   A sample of hydrated sodium sulphate weighing 9.02 g was heated to dryness; the resulting anhydrous compound, Na_2SO_4, weighed 3.98 g.

(a) Calculate the number of moles of water present in each mole of the hydrated compound.

(b) Obtain the formula of the hydrated compound.

11 A sample of a hydrocarbon is burned completely in excess oxygen forming 5.50 g of carbon dioxide and 2.25 g of water. The relative molecular mass of the hydrocarbon is 70.

Calculate:

(a) the empirical formula of the hydrocarbon;

(b) its molecular formula.

12 A 4.95 g sample of an organic compound is burned completely in an excess of oxygen to form 9.90 g of carbon dioxide and 4.05 g of water. No other product is formed.

(a) Calculate the empirical formula of the compound.

(b) Given that the relative molecular mass of the compound is 88, obtain the molecular formula.

13 A 0.867 g sample of an organic compound was burned completely in an excess of oxygen to form 1.87 g of carbon dioxide and 0.765 g of water. No other product is formed. Calculate the empirical formula of the compound.

14 A 3.25 g sample of an organic compound was burned completely in an excess of oxygen to form 7.70 g of carbon dioxide and 3.15 g of water. No other product was formed. Calculate the empirical formula of the compound.

15 A 3.75 g sample of an organic compound was burned completely in an excess of oxygen, forming 9.90 g of carbon dioxide and 2.25 g of water. No other product was formed. Calculate the molecular formula of the compound.

6

The Equilibrium Constant and Partition Coefficient

Often the position of a chemical equilibrium is described by saying, for example, that 'there are more products than reactants at equilibrium' or 'the equilibrium is mainly to the reactant side', or other such phrases. However, statements like that only give a rough idea of the position of equilibrium; a more precise measure is given by the **equilibrium constant**, symbol K.

For a reaction of the type:

$$a\text{A} + b\text{B} + c\text{C} + \cdots \rightarrow p\text{P} + q\text{Q} + r\text{R} + \cdots$$

the equilibrium constant is defined as:

$$K = \frac{[\text{P}]^p[\text{Q}]^q[\text{R}]^r \cdots}{[\text{A}]^a[\text{B}]^b[\text{C}]^c \cdots}$$

where [P] means **the concentration of P** (usually in units of mol l^{-1}). In the case of reactions involving gases, the **pressure** of each gas at equilibrium can be used as a measure of concentration.

It may seem surprising, but, for reasons outwith the scope of this course, the equilibrium constant has *no* unit. It is simply a numerical value. A further point to note is that **pure solids** and **liquids acting as solvents** for the reaction are given concentration values of 1 in the calculation of K. In effect this means that their concentrations do not affect the value of K under different conditions, since multiplying or dividing by 1, or 1 to a power, does not affect the answer. This is because, under different conditions, for example of temperature, the amount of a solid or pure solvent will not vary to any significant extent at equilibrium, in comparison to other reactants whose concentrations will vary considerably.

A particular equilibrium constant is known as a **partition constant**. This applies to a situation where a substance can dissolve in two liquids which are **immiscible**; that is they do not mix, but form two separate layers when put in the same container. If the soluble substance is shaken up with the two immiscible liquids, some of it will dissolve in one layer and some in the other layer. The ratio of the concentrations of the substance in the two layers is a constant for the substances involved and at a given temperature.

For example, consider a substance X which can dissolve in both hexane and water, which are immiscible. If X is shaken up with these liquids, after a time the equilibrium below will become established.

$$X(water) \rightleftharpoons X(hexane)$$

The partition coefficient is simply the equilibrium constant for the above process, i.e.:

$$K = \frac{[X(hexane)]}{[X(water)]}$$

Worked Example 6.1

Calculate the equilibrium constant for the reaction below.

$$N_2(g) + 3H_2(g) \rightleftharpoons 2NH_3(g)$$

The equilibrium concentrations of the substances present are:

$$
\begin{aligned}
&N_2(g){:} &&4 \text{ mol l}^{-1} \\
&H_2(g){:} &&2 \text{ mol l}^{-1} \\
&NH_3(g){:} &&6 \text{ mol l}^{-1}
\end{aligned}
$$

Answer

Firstly we write an expression to describe K for this equilibrium.

$$K = \frac{[NH_3(g)]^2}{[N_2(g)][H_2(g)]^3}$$

We then insert the data:

$$K = \frac{6^2}{4 \times 2^3}$$

$$= \frac{36}{32}$$

$$= \mathbf{1.125}$$

Worked Example 6.2

A monoprotic organic acid A is soluble both in water and hexane. Water and hexane are immiscible (that is, they do not mix). A sample of the acid is thoroughly shaken up with 100 cm³ of water and 100 cm³ of hexane until all the acid is dissolved. After some time the equilibrium below is established.

$$A(\text{hexane}) \rightleftharpoons A(\text{aq})$$

To determine the partition coefficient for this equilibrium, a 25 cm³ sample of each layer was extracted by pipettes and titrated with standard 0.10 mol l⁻¹ sodium hydroxide solution, NaOH(aq). The titres of sodium hydroxide solution were as below:

Aqueous layer: 20.2 cm³
Hexane layer: 5.05 cm³

Calculate:

(a) the concentration of acid in each layer;

(b) the partition coefficient in the ratio [A(aq)] / [A(hexane)].

Answer

(a) The acid is described as monoprotic, meaning that each molecule contains only one H⁺ ion available for neutralisation with alkali.

So, in the titration, 1 mol of the acid reacts with 1 mol of the NaOH(aq).

So the concentration of acid in the aqueous layer is worked out as follows:

Volume of NaOH(aq) = 20.2 cm³ = 0.0202 litres
Concentration of NaOH(aq) = 0.10 mol l⁻¹

So the number of moles of sodium hydroxide = 0.0202 × 0.1 = 0.00202.

This is the number of moles of acid present in the 25 cm³ sample, so the concentration of acid is 0.00202 / 0.025 = **0.0808 mol l⁻¹**.

By the same type of calculation the concentration of acid in the hexane layer is **0.0202 mol l⁻¹**.

(b) The partition coefficient in the ratio [A(aq)] / [A(hexane)] is 0.0808 / 0.0202 = **4**.

PROBLEMS

1   Consider the equilibrium below:

$$PCl_3(g) + Cl_2(g) \rightleftharpoons PCl_5(g)$$

The equilibrium concentrations of the reagents involved, under certain conditions, are:

$$
\begin{aligned}
[PCl_3(g)] &= 0.04 \text{ mol l}^{-1} \\
[Cl_2(g)] &= 0.06 \text{ mol l}^{-1} \\
[PCl_5(g)] &= 0.12 \text{ mol l}^{-1}
\end{aligned}
$$

Calculate the equilibrium constant, K, under the above conditions.

2   In the equilibrium:

$$2NO_2(g) \rightleftharpoons N_2O_4(g)$$

the concentrations of the gases present are:

$$
\begin{aligned}
[NO_2(g)] &= 0.05 \text{ mol l}^{-1} \\
[N_2O_4(g)] &= 0.4 \text{ mol l}^{-1}
\end{aligned}
$$

Calculate the equilibrium constant, K, for the reaction under the above conditions.

3   The esterification of methanol and ethanoic acid to form methyl ethanoate and water is represented by the equation below.

$$CH_3OH(l) + CH_3COOH(l) \rightleftharpoons CH_3COOCH_3(l) + H_2O(l)$$

At equilibrium, the concentrations of the substances present are:

$$
\begin{aligned}
[CH_3OH(l)] &= 0.2 \text{ mol l}^{-1} \\
[CH_3COOH(l)] &= 0.5 \text{ mol l}^{-1} \\
[CH_3COOCH_3(l)] &= 1.2 \text{ mol l}^{-1} \\
[H_2O(l)] &= 0.8 \text{ mol l}^{-1}
\end{aligned}
$$

Calculate the equilibrium constant, K, for the reaction under the above conditions.

4 The decomposition of sulphur trioxide is represented by the following equation.

$$2SO_3(g) \rightleftharpoons 2SO_2(g) + O_2(g)$$

At equilibrium, under certain conditions, the concentrations of the gases are:

$$[SO_3(g)] = 2 \text{ mol } l^{-1}$$
$$[SO_2(g)] = 4 \text{ mol } l^{-1}$$
$$[O_2(g)] = 2 \text{ mol } l^{-1}$$

Calculate the equilibrium constant, K, for the reaction under the above conditions.

5 The reaction of carbon dioxide with hydrogen to form methanol is given by the following equation:

$$CO(g) + 2H_2(g) \rightleftharpoons CH_3OH(g)$$

At equilibrium, the concentrations of the gases under certain conditions are:

$$[CO(g)] = 2.5 \text{ mol } l^{-1}$$
$$[H_2(g)] = 2 \text{ mol } l^{-1}$$
$$[CH_3OH(g)] = 5 \text{ mol } l^{-1}$$

Calculate the equilibrium constant, K, for the reaction under the above conditions.

6 The partial oxidation of methane is shown by the equation below.

$$2CH_4(g) + O_2(g) \rightleftharpoons 2CO(g) + 4H_2(g)$$

At equilibrium, under certain conditions, the concentrations of the gases are:

$$[CH_4(g)] = 0.5 \text{ mol } l^{-1}$$
$$[O_2(g)] = 0.6 \text{ mol } l^{-1}$$
$$[CO(g)] = 0.3 \text{ mol } l^{-1}$$
$$[H_2(g)] = 0.2 \text{ mol } l^{-1}$$

Calculate the equilibrium constant, K, for the reaction under the above conditions.

7   0.2 mol of ethanol and 0.2 mol of methanoic acid are mixed with a few drops of concentrated sulphuric acid catalyst in an empty reaction vessel. After equilibrium is established, it is found that 0.15 mol of the ester, ethyl methanoate, has been formed.

The equation for the reaction taking place is:

$$C_2H_5OH(l) + HCOOH(l) \rightleftharpoons HCOOC_2H_5(l) + H_2O(l)$$

Calculate the equilibrium constant, K, for the reaction under these conditions.

8   1 mol of $H_2(g)$ and 1 mol of $I_2(g)$ are introduced into an empty reaction chamber in which the following reaction takes place.

$$H_2(g) + I_2(g) \rightleftharpoons 2HI(g)$$

After some time, equilibrium is established and it is found that there is 0.6 mol of $HI(g)$ present in the gas mixture. Calculate the equilibrium constant, K, for the reaction under the above conditions.

9   0.5 mol of $CH_4(g)$ and 0.5 mol of $H_2O(g)$ are introduced into an empty, 1 litre, reaction chamber in which the reaction below takes place.

$$CH_4(g) + H_2O(g) \rightleftharpoons CO(g) + 3H_2(g)$$

When equilibrium is established, it is found that there is 0.15 mol of $CO(g)$ present. Calculate the equilibrium constant, K, for the reaction under these conditions.

10   The industrial production of 'freon', $CCl_2F_2(g)$, is represented by the following equation.

$$CCl_4(g) + 2HF(g) \rightleftharpoons CCl_2F_2(g) + 2HCl(g)$$

1 mol of $CCl_4(g)$ and 2 mol of $HF(g)$ are introduced into an empty reaction chamber. When equilibrium is established, it is found that 0.75 mol of 'freon' has been formed. Calculate the equilibrium constant, K, for the reaction under these conditions.

11   Toluene is an organic liquid which is immiscible in water. A different organic substance, X, is soluble in both liquids. A sample of X is shaken up with toluene and water and given time for the equilibrium shown below to stabilise.

$$X(toluene) \rightleftharpoons X(aq)$$

Samples of substance X in each of the layers were analysed. The concentration of X in the toluene layer was found to be 0.253 mol l^{-1}. The concentration of X in the aqueous layer was 0.201 mol l^{-1}. Calculate the partition coefficient for the above equilibrium in the ratio [X(aq)] / [X(toluene)].

12   A monoprotic organic acid, A, is soluble in both ethoxyethane and water. Ethoxyethane and water are immiscible.

The equilibrium relating to the acid between the two solvents is described in the equation below.

$$A(ethoxyethane) \rightleftharpoons A(aq)$$

A 10 cm^3 sample of each solution was extracted by pipette and titrated with standard 0.10 mol l^{-1} sodium hydroxide solution, NaOH(aq).

The sodium hydroxide titre of the ethoxyethane layer was 22.3 cm^3. The titre of the aqueous layer was 14.8 cm^3.

Calculate:

(a)   the concentration of the organic acid in each of the two layers;

(b)   the partition coefficient for this equilibrium, in the ratio [A(aq)] / [A(ethoxyethane)], under the conditions of this analysis.

13   Iodine is an element which can dissolve in aqueous potassium iodide solution and cyclohexane, but the two solvents are immiscible. A quantity of iodine was shaken with samples of the two solvents and given time for the equilibrium below to be established.

$$I_2(aq) \rightleftharpoons I_2(cyclohexane)$$

A 25 cm^3 sample was taken from each layer and analysed by titration with standard 0.250 mol l^{-1} sodium thiosulphate solution, Na$_2$S$_2$O$_3$(aq) using starch as an indicator. (At the endpoint of the titration the blue/black colour of the complex which iodine forms with starch disappears.)

The equation for the titration reaction is:

$$2S_2O_3 + I_2 \rightarrow S_4O_6^{2-} + 2I^-$$

The titres were as below:

Aqueous layer: 12.4 cm^3
Cyclohexane layer: 18.6 cm^3

Calculate:

(a) the concentration of iodine in each layer;

(b) the partition coefficient in the ratio of $[I_2(cyclohexane)] / [I_2(aq)]$.

14   An organic substance, X, of molecular mass 60, can dissolve both in water and in hexane. The two solvents are immiscible. The equation for the equilibrium is given below.

$$X(hexane) \rightleftharpoons X(aq)$$

The partition coefficient for this equilibrium, in the ratio $[X(aq)] / [X(hexane)]$, is 1.42.

A quantity of substance X is shaken up with 50 cm^3 of water and 50 cm^3 of hexane and left until equilibrium is established.

The concentration of X in the hexane layer is analysed and found to be 0.40 mol l^{-1}.

Calculate:

(a) the concentration of X in the aqueous layer;

(b) the mass of X in the aqueous layer.

15   An organic substance, A, of molecular mass 65, is soluble in both toluene and water. The solvents are immiscible. A quantity of substance A was shaken with 100 cm^3 of each solvent until the following equilibrium was established.

$$A(aq) \rightleftharpoons A(toluene)$$

The partition coefficient for this equilibrium, in the ratio [A(toluene)] / [A(aq)], is 1.50.

The aqueous layer was analysed and the concentration of A in this layer was found to be 0.024 mol l^{-1}.

Calculate:

(a) the concentration of substance A in the toluene layer;

(b) the mass of A in the toluene layer.

pH of Solutions and the Ionic Product of Water

The definition of pH is:

$$pH = -\log[H^+(aq)]$$

In this expression, $[H^+(aq)]$ refers to the concentration of $H^+(aq)$.

In all aqueous solutions there is an equilibrium between $H^+(aq)$ and $OH^-(aq)$ ions, and water molecules, represented by the equation below.

$$H_2O(l) \rightleftharpoons H^+(aq) + OH^-(aq)$$

In aqueous solution, the relationship between $[H^+(aq)]$ and $[OH^-(aq)]$ is defined by K_w, the Ionic Product of water.

$$K_w = [H^+(aq)][OH^-(aq)] = 10^{-14} \text{ mol}^2 \text{ l}^{-2} \text{ at } 25\,°C$$

The value of 10^{-14} only applies at 25 °C since a change in temperature will change the position of equilibrium between $H_2O(l)$ molecules and $H^+(aq)$ and $OH^-(aq)$ ions, and therefore change the value of K_w. In all the examples and problems on this topic it will be assumed that the temperature of solutions is 25 °C.

Worked Example 7.1

What is the pH of a solution in which the concentration of hydrogen ions is 0.05 mol l^{-1}?

Answer
We are told that $[H^+(aq)] = 0.05$ mol l^{-1} so we can use the equation below directly.

$$\begin{aligned} pH &= -\log[H^+(aq)] \\ &= -\log 0.05 \\ &= 1.30 \end{aligned}$$

Worked Example 7.2

What is the concentration of hydrogen ions in a solution with a pH of 11.5?

Answer

In order to get $[H^+(aq)]$ from the pH we have to 'unlog' the equation $pH = -\log[H^+(aq)]$ by using the inverse function on a calculator, usually labelled 10^x.

$$[H^+(aq)] = \text{inverse log } (-11.5)$$
$$= 3.16 \times 10^{-12} \text{ mol l}^{-1}$$

Worked Example 7.3

A solution of sulphuric acid, H_2SO_4, has a pH of 2.8. Calculate:

(a) the concentration of hydrogen ions;

(b) the concentration of the acid.

Answer

(a) The value for $[H^+(aq)]$ is calculated exactly as in Worked Example 7.2 and found to be **$1.58 \times 10^{-3} \text{ mol l}^{-1}$**.

(b) Looking at part (b) of the question it might not be obvious that the concentration of hydrogen ions in the sulphuric acid is different from the concentration of the sulphuric acid, but the acid, H_2SO_4, is fully dissociated in aqueous solution, providing **2** moles of $H^+(aq)$ for every **1** mole of H_2SO_4.

So the concentration of H_2SO_4 is *half* the concentration of $H^+(aq)$:

$$0.5 \times 1.58 \times 10^{-3} \text{ mol l}^{-1}$$
$$= 7.92 \times 10^{-4} \text{ mol l}^{-1}$$

PROBLEMS

1   Calculate the pH of a solution of a 0.20 mol l^{-1} solution of hydrochloric acid, HCl.

2   The concentration of hydrogen ions in a solution is $6.24 \times 10^{-8} \text{ mol l}^{-1}$. Calculate the pH of the solution.

3   A weak acid solution has a hydrogen ion concentration of 3.82×10^{-5} mol l^{-1}. Calculate the pH of the solution.

4   Calculate the pH of a 0.182 mol l^{-1} solution of sulphuric acid, H_2SO_4.

5   A solution of sulphuric acid, H_2SO_4, has a concentration of 1.25 mol l^{-1}. Calculate the pH of the solution.

6   A solution of nitric acid, HNO_3, has a pH of 1.57. Calculate the concentration of hydrogen ions present.

7   A lactic acid solution has a pH of 4.87. Calculate the concentration of hydrogen ions in the solution.

8   Calculate the concentration of hydrogen ions in a solution with a pH of 9.8.

9   What is the concentration of hydrogen ions in an alkali solution with a pH of 12.9?

10   A hydrochloric acid solution has a pH of –0.152. Calculate the concentration of the solution.

11   A sodium hydroxide solution, NaOH, has a pH of 12.3. Calculate:

(a) the concentration of hydrogen ions;

(b) the concentration of hydroxide ions.

12   An acid solution has a hydroxide ion concentration of 2.87×10^{-13} mol l^{-1}. Calculate:

(a) the concentration of hydrogen ions;

(b) the pH of the solution.

13   A solution of sodium hydroxide, NaOH, has a concentration of 0.638 mol l^{-1}. Calculate:

(a) the hydrogen ion concentration;

(b) the pH of the solution.

14   The pH of a hydrochloric acid solution is −0.253. Calculate:

(a) the hydrogen ion concentration;

(b) the hydroxide ion concentration.

15   The pH of an ethanoic acid solution is 3.48. Calculate:

(a) the hydrogen ion concentration;

(b) the hydroxide ion concentration.

8

Dissociation Constants and the pH of Weak Acids

The dissociation of a weak monoprotic acid (one which has only one available hydrogen ion per molecule) can be represented as below, taking ethanoic acid solution as an example:

$$CH_3COOH(aq) \rightleftharpoons CH_3COO^-(aq) + H^+(aq)$$

The equilibrium constant for this dissociation, K_a, known as the dissociation constant, is given by the equation:

$$K_a = \frac{[CH_3COO^-(aq)] \times [H^+(aq)]}{[CH_3COOH(aq)]}$$

Since there is one ethanoate ion for every hydrogen ion in solution, this equation can be rewritten as:

$$K_a = \frac{[H^+(aq)]^2}{[CH_3COOH(aq)]}$$

For the dissociation of *any* monoprotic weak acid we can use the general equation

$$HA(aq) \rightleftharpoons H^+(aq) + A^-(aq)$$

where HA(aq) represents the undissociated acid and A$^-$(aq) represents the negative ion produced on dissociation. For any weak monoprotic acid we can define K_a as below.

$$K_a = \frac{[H^+(aq)]^2}{[HA(aq)]} \quad \text{or} \quad K_a = \frac{[H^+(aq)]^2}{c}$$

$$\text{where } c = [HA(aq)].$$

The two equations above are identical except that [HA(aq)] has been abbreviated to c. This abbreviation will be used for the concentration of the undissociated acid in the rest of this topic.

The dissociation constants for selected species are given on page 12 of the Data Book. (For reasons that are outwith the scope of the Advanced Higher course, the dissociation constant has *no* unit.) From the above equation, if we know two of the three quantities, the other can be calculated. The relevant equations are:

$$c = \frac{[H^+(aq)]^2}{K_a} \quad \text{and} \quad [H^+(aq)] = \sqrt{K_a \times c}$$

Worked Example 8.1

A solution of ethanoic acid has a concentration of 0.1 mol l^{-1}. The K_a for ethanoic acid is 1.7×10^{-5}. Calculate the concentration of $H^+(aq)$ in the solution.

Answer
Select the appropriate equation and put in the data.

$$[H^+(aq)] = \sqrt{K_a \times c} = \sqrt{1.7 \times 10^{-5} \times 0.1} = 1.30 \times 10^{-3} \text{ mol } l^{-1}$$

Worked Example 8.2

A solution of butanoic acid has a hydrogen ion concentration of 5.48×10^{-4} mol l^{-1}. Calculate the concentration of the butanoic acid solution using the Data Book value of 1.5×10^{-5} for the K_a of butanoic acid.

Answer
Select the appropriate equation and put in the data.

$$c = \frac{[H^+(aq)]^2}{K_a}$$

$$= \frac{(5.48 \times 10^{-4})^2}{1.5 \times 10^{-5}}$$

$$= 0.0200 \text{ mol } l^{-1}$$

Additional Theory

Just as pH is a useful logarithmic measure of the concentration of hydrogen ions, pK_a is defined as below:

$$pK_a = -\log K_a$$

Page 12 of the Data Book gives pK_a values beside those of K_a. This gives numerical values which are often easier to handle than those of K_a.

pH, pK_a and the concentration of the acid (c), are related by the following important expression.

$$pH = \frac{1}{2}pK_a - \frac{1}{2}\log c$$

An alternative arrangement of this equation is given below.

$$pK_a = 2pH + \log c$$

The use of these equations can be seen in the following Worked Examples.

Worked Example 8.3

What is the pH of a 0.20 mol l^{-1} solution of ethanoic acid?

Answer
From the Data Book, the pK_a of ethanoic acid is 4.76.

$$
\begin{aligned}
pH &= \frac{1}{2}pK_a - \frac{1}{2}\log c \\
&= (0.5 \times 4.76) - (0.5 \times \log 0.2) \\
&= 2.73
\end{aligned}
$$

Worked Example 8.4

A solution of butanoic acid has a pH of 2.67. Calculate the concentration of the solution.

Answer
From the Data Book, the pK_a for butanoic acid is 4.83.

$$
\begin{aligned}
pH &= \frac{1}{2}pK_a - \frac{1}{2}\log c \\
2.67 &= (0.5 \times 4.83) - (0.5 \times \log c) \\
0.255 &= -0.5 \times \log c
\end{aligned}
$$

Dividing each side by −0.5, we now have:

$$-0.51 = \log c$$

Using the inverse log function on a calculator, usually labelled 10^x, we can 'unlog' each side of this equation to give:

$$0.309 = c$$

So the concentration of the solution is **0.309 mol l⁻¹**.

Worked Example 8.5

A 0.20 mol l⁻¹ solution of a weak monoprotic acid has a pH of 2.49. Calculate the pK_a for the acid.

Answer

Using the form of the equation below connecting pH, pK_a and concentration of the acid, we have

$$
\begin{aligned}
pK_a &= 2pH + \log c \\
&= 2 \times 2.49 + \log 0.2 \\
&= 4.98 + (-0.699) \\
&= \mathbf{4.28}
\end{aligned}
$$

PROBLEMS

1   The K_a value for methanoic acid is 1.8×10^{-4}. Calculate the concentration of hydrogen ions in a 0.01 mol l⁻¹ solution of methanoic acid.

2   Use the K_a value for butanoic acid to calculate the concentration of the acid which, in aqueous solution, would have a hydrogen ion concentration of 1.73×10^{-3} mol l⁻¹.

3   Obtain the K_a value for propanoic acid and use it to calculate the concentration of hydrogen ions in a 0.040 mol l⁻¹ solution of the acid.

4   Use the K_a value for hydrofluoric acid to calculate the concentration of the acid which, in aqueous solution, would have a hydrogen ion concentration of 0.0184 mol l⁻¹.

5   Use the K_a value for hydrocyanic acid to calculate the hydrogen ion concentration in a 0.35 mol l⁻¹ solution of the acid.

In Problems 6–15, refer to the Data Book for pK$_a$ values.

6   Calculate the pH of a 0.100 mol l^{-1} solution of ethanoic acid.

7   Calculate the pH of a 0.200 mol l^{-1} solution of methanoic acid.

8   Calculate the pH of a 0.500 mol l^{-1} solution of hydrofluoric acid.

9   Calculate the pH of a 0.15 mol l^{-1} solution of benzoic acid.

10   Calculate the pH of a 0.240 mol l^{-1} solution of butanoic acid.

11   A solution of methanoic acid has a pH of 2.52. Calculate the concentration of the acid.

12   A solution of benzoic acid has a pH of 2.63. Calculate the concentration of the acid.

13   A solution of butanoic acid has a pH of 3.05. Calculate the concentration of the acid.

14   A solution of propanoic acid has a pH of 4.23. Calculate the concentration of the acid.

15   A solution of ethanoic acid has a pH of 3.48. Calculate the concentration of the acid.

16   A 0.1 mol l^{-1} solution of a monoprotic acid has a pH of 2.35. Calculate the pK_a of the acid.

17   A 0.05 mol l^{-1} solution of a monoprotic acid has a pH of 1.58. Calculate the pK_a of the acid.

18   A 0.2 mol l^{-1} solution of a monoprotic acid has a pH of 2.41. Calculate the pK_a of the acid.

19   A 0.15 mol l^{-1} solution of a monoprotic acid has a pH of 1.93. Calculate the pK_a of the acid.

20   A 0.5 mol l^{-1} solution of a monoprotic acid has a pH of 2.57. Calculate the pK_a of the acid.

Buffer Solutions

A buffer is a solution which stays at a nearly constant pH, even when acid or alkali is added to it, or when it is diluted.

- An acid buffer consists of a mixture of a weak acid and a salt of this acid formed from a strong alkali: for example, a mixture of ethanoic acid and sodium ethanoate solutions.

- A basic buffer consists of a weak base and a salt of this base formed from a strong acid: for example, a mixture of ammonia and ammonium sulphate solutions.

The pH of an acid buffer can be calculated using the following equation, where the square brackets mean 'concentration of'.

$$pH = pK_a - \log \frac{[acid]}{[salt]}$$

An alternative version of this is:

$$pH = pK_a + \log \frac{[salt]}{[acid]}$$

Knowing the concentrations of acid and salt, the pH of the buffer can be obtained, using the pK_a of the weak acid given in the Data Book.

Knowing the pH the buffer has to be, and the pK_a of the weak acid, the ratio of [acid] : [salt] can be obtained from the first equation (or [salt] : [acid] from the second). The buffer can then be made up by using *any concentrations of acid and salt in that ratio*.

Worked Example 9.1

Calculate the pH of a buffer solution containing 0.10 mol l⁻¹ ethanoic acid and 0.20 mol l⁻¹ sodium ethanoate.

Answer
The pK_a value of 4.76 for ethanoic acid is obtained from the Data Book, page 12.

Using the former of the two above equations, we have

$$pH = pK_a - \log \frac{[acid]}{[salt]}$$

$$= 4.76 - \log \frac{0.20}{0.20}$$

$$= 4.76 - \log 0.5$$

$$= 4.76 - (-0.301)$$

$$= 5.06$$

Using the latter of the two above equations, we have:

$$pH = pK_a + \log \frac{[salt]}{[acid]}$$

$$= 4.76 + \log \frac{0.20}{0.10}$$

$$= 4.76 + \log 2$$

$$= 4.76 + 0.301$$

$$= 5.06$$

Worked Example 9.2

What concentrations of methanoic acid and potassium methanoate would be required to make a buffer solution with a pH of 4.16?

Answer
The pK_a value for methanoic acid, obtained from the Data Book, is 3.75.

Using the latter of the two equations given earlier, we have

$$pH = pK_a + \log \frac{[salt]}{[acid]}$$

$$4.16 = 3.75 + \log \frac{[salt]}{[acid]}$$

$$0.41 = \log \frac{[salt]}{[acid]}$$

To remove the log from this expression, we 'unlog' each side of the equation by using the inverse log function on a calculator, usually labelled 10^x, giving

$$\frac{[\text{salt}]}{[\text{acid}]} = 2.57$$

This tells us that a ratio of 2.57 mol of potassium methanoate to 1 mol of methanoic acid will give the required pH for the buffer. *Any* mixture in this ratio in *any* volume of water will give this pH.

If the former of the two equations had been used, we would have arrived at the expression:

$$\frac{[\text{acid}]}{[\text{salt}]} = 0.389$$

At first sight this looks like a completely different answer from that previously calculated, but the ratio 2.57 for [salt]/[acid] is identical to that of 0.389 for [acid]/[salt] (allowing for rounding which took place in the calculations.) We can get from one expression to the other by taking the reciprocal of each side of the equation. (Reciprocal means '1 divided by', so, for example, the reciprocal of x is $\frac{1}{x}$ (or x^{-1}).

PROBLEMS

1   Calculate the pH of a buffer comprising 0.20 mol l⁻¹ ethanoic acid and 0.50 mol l⁻¹ sodium ethanoate solution

2   Calculate the pH of a buffer made from a mixture of 0.50 mol of butanoic acid and 0.20 mol of potassium butanoate dissolved to make 1 litre of aqueous solution.

3   A buffer contains a mixture of benzoic acid and sodium benzoate at concentrations of 0.10 and 0.40 mol l⁻¹ respectively. Calculate the pH of the buffer.

4   A buffer is made from a mixture of propanoic acid and sodium propanoate solutions, both at concentrations of 0.10 mol l⁻¹. Calculate the pH of the buffer.

5   Calculate the pH of a buffer made from a mixture of 0.20 mol of methanoic acid and 0.50 mol of sodium methanoate in aqueous solution.

6   Calculate the pH of a buffer made by dissolving 6.00 g of ethanoic acid, CH_3COOH, and 4.10 g of sodium ethanoate, CH_3COONa, in aqueous solution.

7   A buffer solution is made by dissolving 2.76 g of methanoic acid, HCOOH, and 5.44 g of sodium methanoate, HCOONa, in water. Calculate the pH of the buffer.

8   Calculate the pH of the buffer solution made by dissolving 24.4 g of benzoic acid, C_6H_5COOH, and 7.20 g of sodium benzoate, C_6H_5COONa, in water.

9   A buffer solution is made by dissolving 2.96 g of propanoic acid, C_2H_5COOH, and 7.68 g of sodium propanoate, C_2H_5COONa, in water. Calculate the pH of the buffer.

10   Calculate the pH of the buffer solution made by dissolving 2.40 g of ethanoic acid, CH_3COOH, and 1.64 g of sodium ethanoate, CH_3COONa, in water.

11   A buffer containing a solution of methanoic acid and sodium methanoate is made up to pH 3.42. Calculate the molar proportion of acid to salt (or salt to acid) which would be needed to obtain this pH.

12   A buffer containing ethanoic acid and its sodium salt, sodium ethanoate, has a pH of 5.16. Calculate the molar proportion of the acid to salt (or salt to acid) in this buffer.

13   A buffer solution with a pH of 4.76 contains a mixture of benzoic acid and sodium benzoate. Calculate the molar proportion of the acid to the salt (or salt to acid) present.

14   A solution containing a mixture of propanoic acid and potassium propanoate is a buffer with a pH of 4.32. What molar proportion of acid to salt (or salt to acid) would be needed to prepare this buffer?

15   A buffer is made from a solution containing a mixture of butanoic acid and its sodium salt, sodium butanoate. What molar proportion of acid to salt (or salt to acid) would be required to produce a buffer solution with a pH of 4.47?

10

Using Bond Enthalpies

In a chemical reaction, bonds within the reactant molecules get broken and new bonds are made as the products are formed. For example, consider the burning of hydrogen to form water vapour represented by the equation below:

$$2H_2(g) + O_2(g) \rightarrow 2H_2O(g)$$

This reaction can be considered by means of the diagrams below:

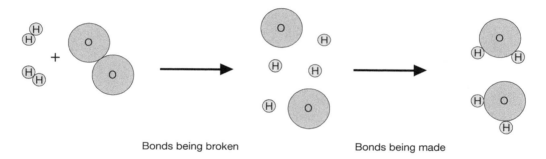

Bonds being broken   Bonds being made

It is possible to calculate the amount of energy involved in bond breaking and bond making steps such as those shown above. These energy values are listed on page 9 of the Data Book under the title 'Selected Bond and Mean Bond Enthalpies'.

The bond enthalpy refers to the amount of energy required to break 1 mol of a particular bond to produce gaseous atoms, or the energy given out when 1 mol of a bond is made from gaseous atoms. The table entitled 'Mean Bond Enthalpies' uses the term 'mean' to imply average. In this table each of the bonds could be present in a range of different compounds. For example the C–H bond is present in alkanes, alkenes, alcohols and many other types of compound. The mean bond enthalpy of C–H is an average of the C–H bond enthalpies in these different compounds. An important point to note about the use of these average values is that a calculated ΔH for a chemical reaction may not be *exactly* the accepted Data Book value, although it should be very close.

The other table on page 9 of the Data Book, entitled 'Bond Enthalpies', contains examples of bonds which can *only* exist in the element or compound shown, and there is therefore no need to calculate an average value.

The use of bond enthalpies can be seen in the following Worked Examples.

Worked Example 10.1

Calculate the enthalpy change (ΔH) for the combustion of hydrogen to form water vapour (as illustrated above) using bond enthalpy data. The balanced equation is repeated below.

$$2H_2(g) + O_2(g) \rightarrow 2H_2O(g)$$

Answer
The data is set out as shown below:

Bond breaking (energy put in, kJ)	Bond making (energy given out, kJ)
2 mol of H–H = 2 × 432 = 864	4 mol of O–H= 4 × 458 = 1832
1 mol of O=O = 497	
Total energy put in = + 1361 kJ	**Total energy given out = –1832 kJ**

The energy put in has been given a positive sign (+) to emphasise that energy has been *put in* to the reactants to break their bonds. A negative sign (–) is given to the energy given out to show that energy has been *given out* from the products as new bonds are made.

The enthalpy change (ΔH) is simply these two values added together. That is:

$$\Delta H = +1361 - 1832$$
$$= -471 \text{ kJ mol}^{-1}$$

Since this energy value represents the enthalpy change (ΔH) *per mole of the equation as written*, we can say that the ΔH for the reaction is –471 kJ mol^{-1}. This is the quantity of heat energy given out when **2 mol** of $H_2(g)$ burns according to the equation given. If we wanted the quantity of heat given out when **1 mol** of $H_2(g)$ burned to form $H_2O(g)$ we would need to divide that value by 2, giving us –235.5 kJ mol^{-1}.

Additional Theory

Three energy terms which students may not be familiar with now need to be introduced.

● **Enthalpy of Sublimation**

The enthalpy of sublimation is the energy required to convert 1 mol of a solid element into separate atoms in the gas state. The most common example of this that we will come across is the enthalpy of sublimation of carbon defined by the equation and ΔH value below:

$$C(s) \rightarrow C(g) \quad \Delta H = 715 \text{ kJ mol}^{-1}$$

This definition and ΔH value are given on page 9 of the Data Book.

● **Standard Molar Enthalpy of Atomisation**

The standard molar enthalpy of atomisation is the energy required to produce 1 mol of separate, gas state, atoms of an element from its usual room temperature state. Data for selected elements is given on page 17 of the Data Book.

For example, the standard molar enthalpies of atomisation of hydrogen, carbon and phosphorus are defined, respectively, by the equations and ΔH values given below:

$$\frac{1}{2}H_2(g) \rightarrow H(g) \quad \Delta H = 216 \text{ kJ mol}^{-1}$$
$$C(s) \rightarrow C(g) \quad \Delta H = 715 \text{ kJ mol}^{-1}$$
$$P(s) \rightarrow P(g) \quad \Delta H = 317 \text{ kJ mol}^{-1}$$

It is worth noting that the ΔH in the first equation is *half* that for the bond enthalpy of hydrogen which is represented by the equation and ΔH value below:

$$H_2(g) \rightarrow 2H(g) \quad \Delta H = 432 \text{ kJ mol}^{-1}$$

(The bond enthalpy refers to breaking the bonds in 1 mol of H–H bonds, i.e. $H_2(g)$, forming **2 mol** of H atoms; the standard molar enthalpy of atomisation refers to forming **1 mol** of H atoms.)

Note also that the standard molar enthalpy of atomisation of carbon is identical to the enthalpy of sublimation of carbon. (Compare equations and ΔH values given above, and in the Data Book, to confirm this.)

● **Enthalpy of Formation**

The enthalpy of formation, ΔH_f, is defined as the enthalpy change which takes place when 1 mol of a compound is formed from its elements, with all the substances in their standard states, i.e. at their normal states at 25 °C and 1 atmosphere pressure. For example, the enthalpy of formation of ethanoic acid, CH_3COOH, is defined by the equation and ΔH_f value below.

$$2C(s) + 2H_2(g) + O_2(g) \rightarrow CH_3COOH(l) \quad \Delta H_f = -487 \text{ kJ mol}^{-1}$$

Worked Example 10.2

Calculate the enthalpy of formation of chloroethane, C_2H_5Cl, using bond enthalpy data and the enthalpy of sublimation of carbon. The equation for the reaction is given below.

$$2C(s) + 2\tfrac{1}{2}H_2(g) + \tfrac{1}{2}Cl_2(g) \rightarrow C_2H_5Cl(g)$$

Answer

The data can be set out as the bond breaking and making steps, as in the previous Worked Example. However, before doing so, it is important to draw out the extended structure of chloroethane to help avoid accidentally missing out any bonds in the calculation.

$$
\begin{array}{ccc}
 & H & H \\
 & | & | \\
H - & C - & C - Cl \\
 & | & | \\
 & H & H
\end{array}
$$

Bond breaking (energy put in, kJ)

2 mol of C(s) $= 2 \times 715 = 1430$

$2\tfrac{1}{2}$ mol of H–H $= 2\tfrac{1}{2} \times 432 = 1080$

$\tfrac{1}{2}$ mol of Cl–Cl $= \tfrac{1}{2} \times 243 = 121.5$

Total energy put in $= +2631.5$

Bond making (energy given out, kJ)

1 mol of C–C $= 346$

1 mol of C–Cl $= 326$

5 mol of C–H $= 5 \times 414 = 2070$

Total energy given out $= -2742$

$$\Delta H \text{ for reaction} = 2631.5 - 2742$$
$$= -110.5 \text{ kJ mol}^{-1}$$

Note

The enthalpy value of 715 kJ in the first line of the bond breaking column referred to the enthalpy of sublimation of carbon and *not* the C–C bond enthalpy. The former refers to breaking bonds in solid carbon; the latter refers to breaking the C–C bond in carbon-containing compounds.

Worked Example 10.3

The equation for the enthalpy of formation of ethyne and the value for ΔH_f are given below.

$$2C(s) + H_2(g) \rightarrow C_2H_2(g) \quad \Delta H_f = 227 \text{ kJ mol}^{-1}$$

Use the enthalpy of sublimation (or atomsation) of carbon and the bond enthalpies of the H–H and C–H bonds to calculate the bond enthalpy of the C≡C bond in ethyne.

Answer
The data is set out as in previous Worked Examples. Since the question is asking for the bond enthalpy of C≡C this is entered as x, representing the unknown value.

Bond breaking (energy put in, kJ)

2 mol of C(s) = 2 × 715 =	1430
1 mol of H–H	=	432
Total energy put in	= + 1862 kJ

Bond making (energy given out, kJ)

2 mol of C–H = 2 × 414 =	828
1 mol of C≡C =	x
Total energy given out = –(828 + x) kJ

So the ΔH for the reaction, ΔH_f, which we know to be 227 kJ mol^{-1}, can be described as below, all values in kJ.

$$\Delta H_f = 227 = 1862 - (828 + x)$$

Solving the above equation gives us $x = 807$ kJ mol^{-1} as the calculated value of the bond enthalpy of the C≡C bond.

So the bond enthalpy of C≡C is **807 kJ mol^{-1}**

Note
This calculated value applies *only* to the C≡C in ethyne. The Data Book value of 835 kJ mol^{-1} is a mean bond enthalpy, i.e. an average of the enthalpy values for this bond in a range of different compounds.

PROBLEMS

1 Use bond enthalpy data to calculate the ΔH for the reaction below.

$$2F_2(g) + 2H_2O(g) \rightarrow 4HF(g) + O_2(g)$$

2 Use bond enthalpy data to calculate the ΔH for the reaction below.

$$CH_4(g) + 2O_2(g) \rightarrow CO_2(g) + 2H_2O(g)$$

3 Use bond enthalpy data to calculate the ΔH for the reaction below.

$$CH_4(g) + Cl_2(g) \rightarrow CH_3Cl(g) + HCl(g)$$

4 Use bond enthalpy data to calculate the ΔH for the fluorination of ethene shown by the equation below.

$$C_2H_4(g) + F_2(g) \rightarrow C_2H_4F_2(g)$$

5 The hydration of ethene to ethanol is represented by the equation below.

$$C_2H_4(g) + H_2O(g) \rightarrow C_2H_5OH(g)$$

Calculate the ΔH for this reaction using bond enthalpy data.

6 Use bond enthalpy data to calculate the ΔH for the chlorination of ethanal to trichloroethanal, represented by the equation below.

$$CH_3CHO(g) + 3Cl_2(g) \rightarrow CCl_3CHO(g) + 3HCl(g)$$

7 Calculate the ΔH for the reaction below using bond enthalpy data.

$$C_2H_2(g) + H_2O(g) \rightarrow CH_3CHO(g)$$

8 The enthalpy of formation of phosphine, $PH_3(g)$, is 5 kJ mol^{-1}. Use the bond enthalpy of H–H and the standard molar enthalpy of atomisation of phosphorus to calculate the bond enthalpy of the P–H bond in phosphine.

9 The enthalpy of formation of hydrogen sulphide, $H_2S(g)$, is –17 kJ mol^{-1}. Use this information, bond enthalpy data and the standard molar enthalpy of atomisation of sulphur to calculate the S–H bond enthalpy.

10   The bond enthalpy of Si–H is 318 kJ mol^{-1}. Use this information, bond enthalpy data and the standard molar enthalpy of atomisation of silicon to calculate the ΔH for the reaction below.

$$Si_2H_6(g) \rightarrow 2Si(s) + 3H_2(g)$$

Consider three imaginary chemical reactions and their ΔH values shown below.

Reaction 1 $A \rightarrow B$ $\Delta H_1 = 40$ kJ mol^{-1}
Reaction 2 $B \rightarrow C$ $\Delta H_2 = -30$ kJ mol^{-1}
Reaction 3 $C \rightarrow D$ $\Delta H_3 = -20$ kJ mol^{-1}

We can plot these enthalpy changes on the enthalpy diagram below.

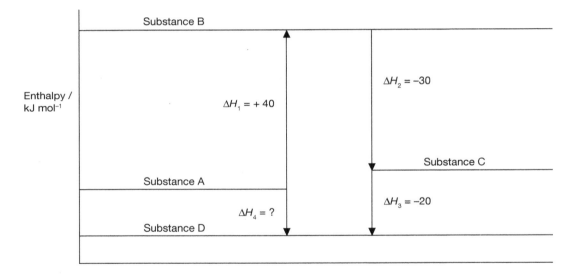

The ΔH information for Reactions 1, 2 and 3 can be used to calculate the ΔH for the reaction below.

Reaction 4 $A \rightarrow D$

Although it will be obvious from a quick look at the diagram that the value for ΔH_4 is -10 kJ mol^{-1}, the real-life problems in this section involve more complex equations and with less easy ΔH values. There are two ways in which an unknown value can be obtained systematically. These are considered next, still with reference to the above diagram.

METHOD 1

Ignoring, for now, the directions of the arrows and the signs of the ΔH values, we can say that the 'distance' of the unknown ΔH_4 is the 'distance' between B and D minus the 'distance' between A and B.

The 'distance' between B and D is $30 + 20 = 50$ kJ mol^{-1} and that between A and B is 40 kJ mol^{-1}. So the 'distance' between A and D is $50 - 40 = 10$ kJ mol^{-1}.

Since ΔH_4 is the enthalpy change for the reaction going from A to D, *down* the diagram, this must be a *decrease* in enthalpy, that is, ΔH_4 has a *negative* value.

$$\text{So } \Delta H_4 = -10 \text{ kJ mol}^{-1}.$$

METHOD 2

The enthalpy change for Reaction 4, labelled ΔH_4 on the diagram, can be carried out by the followng steps, this time taking into account the *direction* and therefore the *sign* of ΔH of each step.

Reaction 1	A $\rightarrow$ B	ΔH_1 = +40 kJ mol^{-1} followed by
Reaction 2	B $\rightarrow$ C	ΔH_2 = −30 kJ mol^{-1} followed by
Reaction 3	C $\rightarrow$ D	ΔH_3 = −20 kJ mol^{-1}

This means that:

$$\begin{aligned} \Delta H_4 &= \Delta H_1 + \Delta H_2 + \Delta H_3 \\ &= +40 - 30 - 20 \\ &= -10 \text{ kJ mol}^{-1} \end{aligned}$$

The following Worked Examples involve real chemical processes of the type that can be expected at Advanced Higher level. Students will be able to judge for themselves which of the two methods they are more comfortable with.

Worked Example 11.1

Consider the following enthalpy diagram, known as a Born-Haber cycle, which shows the steps involved in the formation of 1 mol of $Na^+Cl^-(s)$ from its elements in their standard states, i.e. at 25 °C (298 K) and 1 atmosphere pressure. This diagram, and all others in this chapter, is not drawn to scale.

The enthalpy of formation of $Na^+Cl^-(s)$, labelled ΔH_6 on the diagram, relates to the reaction below.

$$Na(s) + \tfrac{1}{2}Cl_2(g) \rightarrow Na^+Cl^-(s)$$

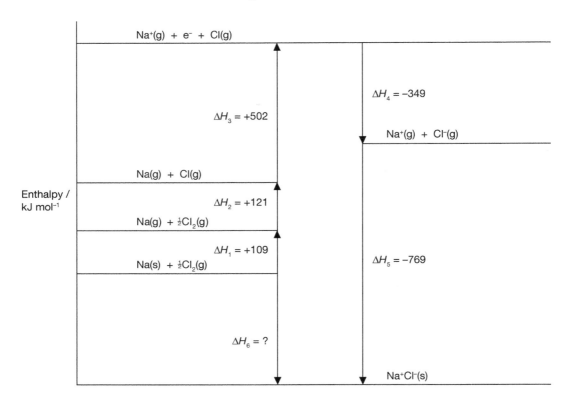

The names of the energy changes in the diagram are given below.

Calculate the value for ΔH_6 from the data given.

ΔH_1 = enthalpy of atomisation of Na

ΔH_2 = enthalpy of atomisation of Cl *or* $\tfrac{1}{2}$ × bond enthalpy of Cl–Cl. The value of 121 kJ mol^{-1} is the Data Book value for the former term; this is the value used in the following calculation. If the latter term had been used, the value would have been 121.5 kJ mol^{-1}. This does not represent a chemical difference, but one to do with rounding of data to give whole numbers in the Data Book. Either value would be correct.

ΔH_3 = ionisation energy of Na

ΔH_4 = electron affinity of Cl

ΔH_5 = lattice enthalpy of NaCl

Tables of selected data, including the above, are give in the SQA's National Qualifications Chemistry Data Book. It should be noted that the definitions of some energy changes are given in this Data Book.

The calculation ΔH_6 can be done by Method 1, the 'distance' method, or by Method 2, a more mathematical approach.

METHOD 1

Ignoring, for now, the signs indicating the direction of enthalpy changes (ΔH + or −), we can see from the diagram that the 'distance' ΔH_6 is the same as the total of the 'distances' ΔH_4 and ΔH_5 minus the total of the 'distances' of ΔH_1, ΔH_2 and ΔH_3.

The 'distance' of $\Delta H_4 + \Delta H_5 = 349 + 769 = 1118$ kJ mol^{-1}

The 'distance' of ΔH_1, ΔH_2 and $\Delta H_3 = 109 + 121 + 502 = 732$ kJ mol^{-1}

So the 'distance' of $\Delta H_6 = 1118 - 732 = 386$ kJ mol^{-1}

This calculated 'distance' is the *positive* value of ΔH_6. However, the *direction* of ΔH_6 is *negative*, indicated by the downward arrow.

$$\text{So } \Delta H_6 = -386 \text{ kJ mol}^{-1}$$

METHOD 2

From the enthalpy diagram, ΔH_6 can be obtained by following the route ΔH_1 then ΔH_2, ΔH_3, ΔH_4, and, finally, ΔH_5.

So, paying careful attention to the signs of these processes, we have:

$$\Delta H_6 = \Delta H_1 + \Delta H_2 + \Delta H_3 + \Delta H_4 + \Delta H_5$$
$$= 109 + 121 + 502 - 349 - 769 = -386 \text{ kJ mol}^{-1}$$

So $\Delta H_6 = -386$ kJ mol^{-1}

Worked Example 11.2

Consider the enthalpy diagram which shows the various energy steps in the formation of lithium chloride from its elements. Use the data provided to calculate ΔH_1, which represents the enthalpy of atomisation of lithium.

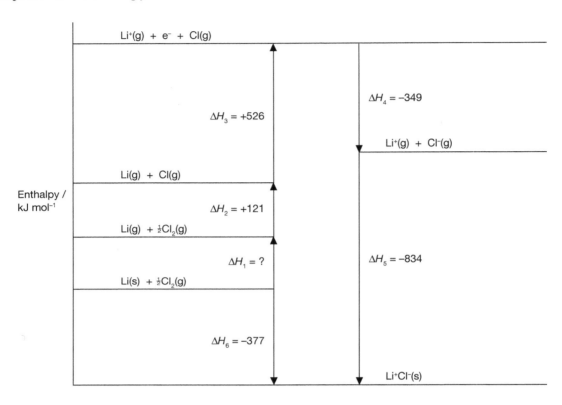

Answer

METHOD 1

The 'distance' of ΔH_1 is the total 'distance' of ΔH_4 and ΔH_5 minus the total 'distance' of ΔH_3, ΔH_2 and ΔH_6.

The total 'distance' of ΔH_4 and ΔH_5 = 349 + 834 = 1183 kJ mol⁻¹.
The total 'distance' of ΔH_3, ΔH_2 and ΔH_6 = 526 + 121 + 377 = 1024 kJ mol⁻¹.

So the 'distance' of ΔH_1 = 1183 − 1024 = 159 kJ mol⁻¹.

ΔH_1 is a *positive* enthalpy change, as shown by the upward arrow on the diagram.

So ΔH_1 = 159 kJ mol⁻¹.

METHOD 2

ΔH_1 can be achieved by carrying out the following steps in order (going anti-clockwise through the diagram).

ΔH_6 followed by
the *opposite* of ΔH_5 followed by
the *opposite* of ΔH_4 followed by
the *opposite* of ΔH_3 followed by
the *opposite* of ΔH_2

Noting that if we use a ΔH step in the opposite direction we must change the sign of the enthalpy change, we have:

$$
\begin{aligned}
\Delta H_1 &= \Delta H_6 - \Delta H_5 - \Delta H_4 - \Delta H_3 - \Delta H_2 \\
&= -377 - (-834) - (-349) - (526) - (121) \\
&= -377 + 834 + 349 - 526 - 121 \\
&= \mathbf{159\ kJ\ mol^{-1}}
\end{aligned}
$$

It will be obvious that the use of Method 2 in this example needs considerable care to avoid a mistake!

Worked Example 11.3

The enthalpy of solution of potassium fluoride is represented by the following equation and is labelled ΔH_4 on the enthalpy diagram on the following page.

$$K^+F^-(s) \rightarrow K^+(aq) + F^-(aq)$$

Calculate the enthalpy of solution of potassium fluoride using the diagram and data.

ΔH_1 = the lattice (breaking) enthalpy of K^+F^-
ΔH_2 = the hydration enthalpy of K^+
ΔH_3 = the hydration enthalpy of F^-

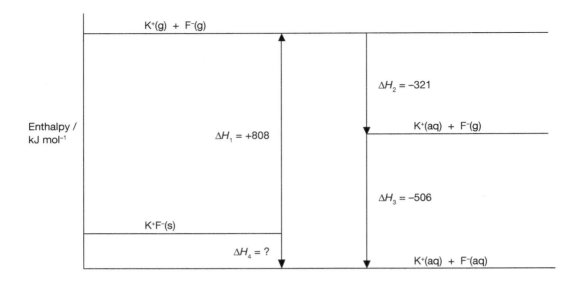

METHOD 1

The 'distance' shown by ΔH_4 is the same as the total 'distance' of ΔH_2 and ΔH_3 minus the 'distance' of ΔH_1. So, ignoring the negative signs involved, as in the previous Worked Examples, the 'distance' of $\Delta H_4 = 321 + 506 - 808 = 19$ kJ mol^{-1}

But since ΔH_4 is a *negative* enthalpy change, indicated by a downward arrow on the diagram, we conclude that

$$\Delta H_4 = -19 \text{ kJ mol}^{-1}$$

METHOD 2

The enthalpy change ΔH_4 can be obtained by carrying out the enthalpy steps labelled ΔH_1 followed by ΔH_2 and then ΔH_3.

$$\text{So } \Delta H_4 = \Delta H_1 + \Delta H_2 + \Delta H_3$$
$$= 808 - 321 - 506$$
$$= -19 \text{ kJ mol}^{-1}$$

1   Consider the enthalpy diagram below, which shows the enthalpy steps in the formation of potassium chloride.

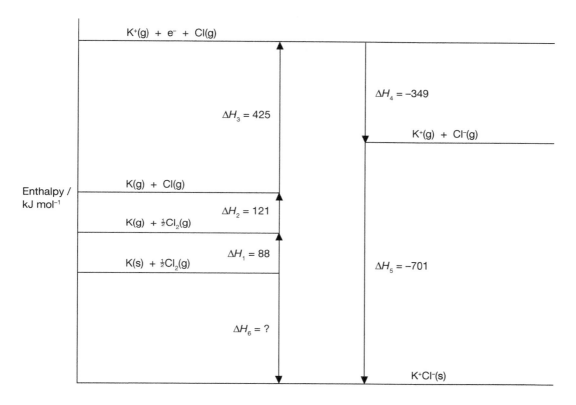

Enthalpy change values are entered on the diagram. Use these to calculate ΔH_6, the enthalpy of formation of potassium chloride.

2   The diagram below shows the enthalpy steps involved in the formation of lithium fluoride from its elements.

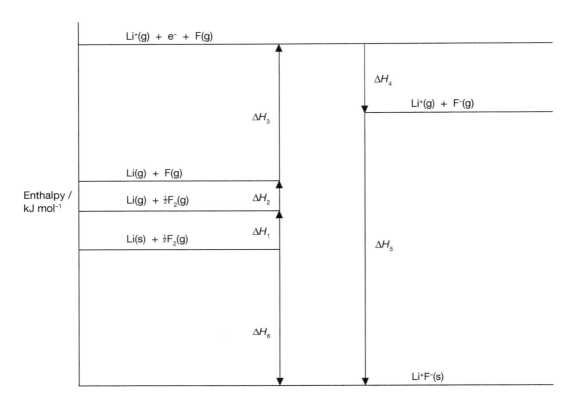

ΔH_1 = the atomisation enthalpy of Li
ΔH_2 = the atomisation enthalpy of F (or $\frac{1}{2}$ × the bond enthalpy of F–F)
ΔH_3 = the first ionisation energy of Li
ΔH_4 = the electron affinity of F
ΔH_5 = the lattice (making) enthalpy of LiF
ΔH_6 = the enthalpy of formation of LiF

(a) Obtain the values for ΔH_1 to ΔH_5 from the Data Book.

(b) Use these values to calculate ΔH_6.

3 The enthalpy diagram below shows the energy changes in the formation of rubidium fluoride from its elements.

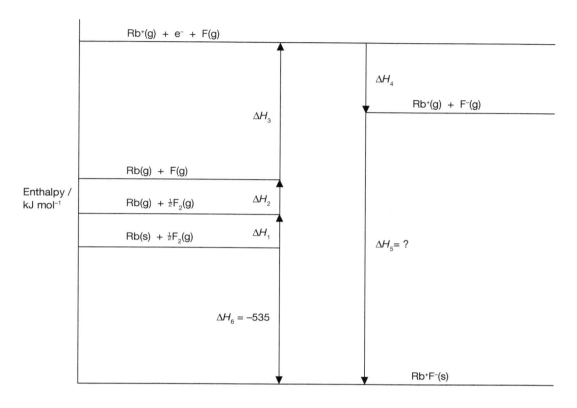

(a) Obtain the values for ΔH_1 to ΔH_4 from the Data Book.

(b) Use these values, and that for the enthalpy of formation of RbF, shown as ΔH_6, with a value of -535 kJ mol^{-1}, to calculate the lattice enthalpy of RbF, shown as ΔH_5.

4   Consider the enthalpy diagram showing the energy steps in the formation of magnesium chloride from its elements.

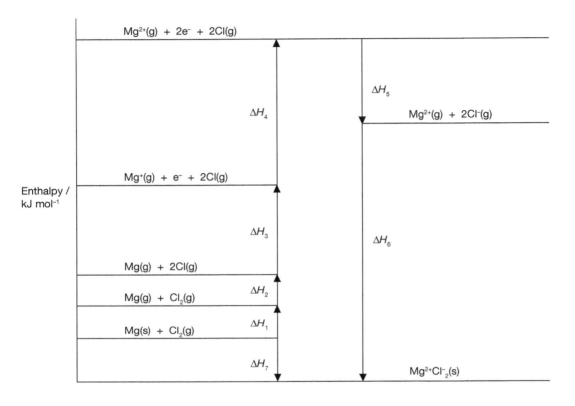

(a) Obtain the values for ΔH_1 to ΔH_6 from the Data Book.

(b) Use these values to calculate ΔH_7, the enthalpy of formation of $MgCl_2$.

5   Consider the enthalpy diagram showing the energy steps in the formation of nickel(II) fluoride from its elements.

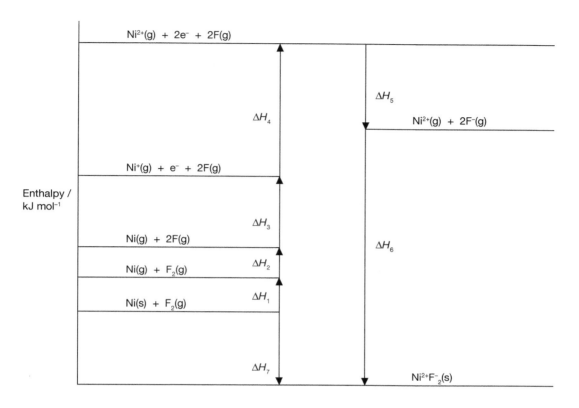

(a) Obtain the values for ΔH_1 to ΔH_6 from the Data Book.

(b) Calculate the value for ΔH_7, the enthalpy of formation of NiF_2.

6   Consider the enthalpy diagram which shows the energy steps in the dissolving of potassium bromide in water.

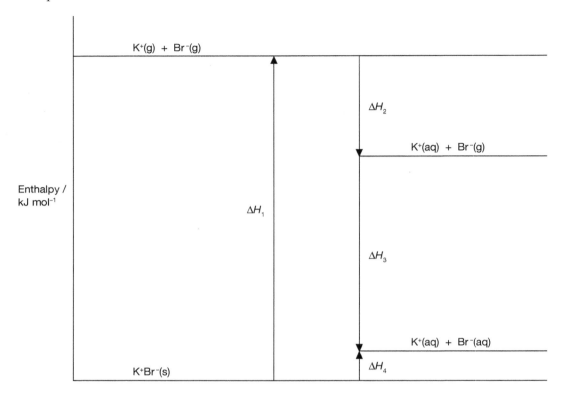

The processes shown are as follows:

ΔH_1 = lattice (breaking) enthalpy of KBr
ΔH_2 = hydration enthalpy of K^+
ΔH_3 = hydration enthalpy of Br^-
ΔH_4 = enthalpy of solution of KBr

(a) Obtain the values for ΔH_1, ΔH_2 and ΔH_3 from the Data Book.

(b) Use these values to calculate ΔH_4.

7   The diagram below shows energy steps relating to the dissolving of sodium bromide in water.

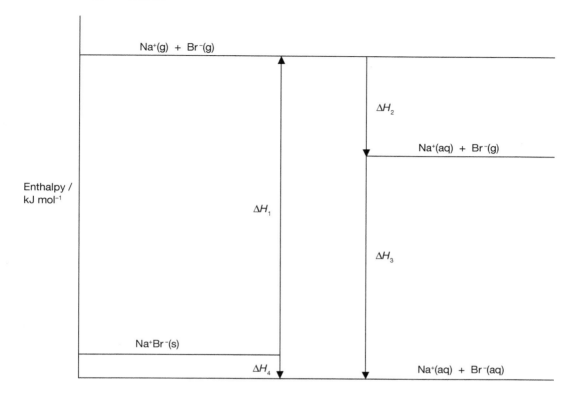

(a)   Obtain values for ΔH_1, ΔH_2 and ΔH_3 from the Data Book.

(b)   Use these values to calculate ΔH_4, the enthalpy of solution of NaBr.

8 The enthalpy diagram below shows the steps involved in dissolving lithium chloride to form an aqueous solution.

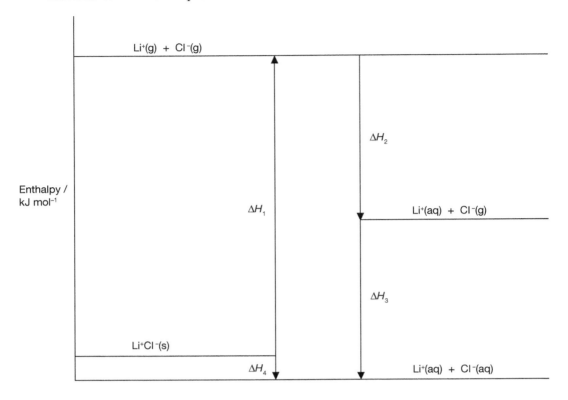

(a) Use the Data Book to obtain values for ΔH_1 to ΔH_3.

(b) Calculate ΔH_4.

9   The enthalpy diagram below shows the steps involved in dissolving magnesium fluoride to form an aqueous solution.

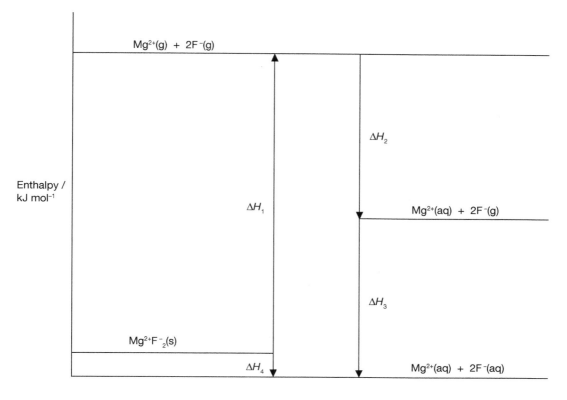

(a) Use the Data Book to obtain values for ΔH_1, ΔH_2 and ΔH_3.

(b) Calculate ΔH_4.

10   Consider the enthalpy diagram below, which shows energy steps in the dissolving of strontium chloride to form an aqueous solution.

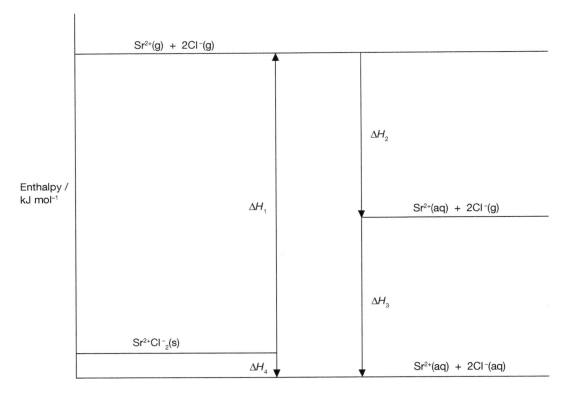

(a) Obtain values for ΔH_1, ΔH_2 and ΔH_3 from the Data Book.

(b) Calculate ΔH_4, the enthalpy of solution of strontium chloride.

$\Delta H°$, $\Delta S°$ and $\Delta G°$

Calculating $\Delta H°$ from Standard Enthalpies of Formation

$\Delta H°$ for a reaction can be obtained by using the standard enthalpies of formation, $\Delta H°_f$, of the substances involved.

The standard enthalpy of formation, $\Delta H°_f$, is defined as the ΔH when a compound is formed from its elements in their usual, room temperature, states. By definition this means that elements have a zero enthalpy of formation. Some enthalpy of formation values are given in the Data Book, page 9. (Note that the superscript $°$ means 'measured under standard conditions', usually 25 °C and 1 atmosphere pressure.)

$\Delta H°$ can be calculated for a reaction by subtracting the total enthalpies of formation of the reactants from the total enthalpies of formation of the products. This is often expressed using the Greek capital letter S, called sigma, symbol Σ, which is used in mathematics to mean 'the sum of'.

$$\Delta H° = \Sigma \Delta H°_f (\text{products}) - \Sigma \Delta H°_f (\text{reactants})$$

This can be seen in the following Worked Example.

Worked Example 12.1

The enthalpies of formation of some substances are given below.

Substance	$\Delta H°_f$/kJ mol^{-1}
$Al_2O_3(s)$	−1676
$H_2(g)$	0
$Al(s)$	0
$H_2O(l)$	−286

Calculate the $\Delta H°$ for the following reaction using the above data.

$$Al_2O_3(s) + 3H_2(g) \rightarrow 2Al(s) + 3H_2O(l)$$

Answer

$$\Delta H° = \Sigma \Delta H°_f \text{(products)} - \Sigma \Delta H°_f \text{(reactants)}$$
$$= \{(3 \times -286) + (2 \times 0)\} - \{(-1676) + (3 \times 0)\}$$
$$= 818 \text{ kJ mol}^{-1}$$

Calculating $\Delta S°$ from Standard Entropy Values

The standard entropy change, $\Delta S°$, for a reaction can be obtained by subtracting the total standard entropies of the reactants from those of the products. This is very similar to calculating $\Delta H°$ from $\Delta H°_f$ data as in the previous section. The equation describing this is given below.

$$\Delta S° = \Sigma S°\text{(products)} - \Sigma S°\text{(reactants)}$$

Worked Example 12.2

Calculate the $\Delta S°$ for the following reaction using the $S°$ data below.

$$Al_2O_3(s) + 3H_2(g) \rightarrow 2Al(s) + 3H_2O(l)$$

Substance	$S°/\text{J mol}^{-1} \text{ K}^{-1}$
Al(s)	28
Al_2O_3(s)	51
H_2(g)	131
H_2O(l)	70

Answer

$$\Delta S° = \Sigma S°\text{(products)} - \Sigma S°\text{(reactants)}$$
$$= \{(3 \times 70) + (2 \times 28)\} - \{(51) + (3 \times 131)\}$$
$$= -178 \text{ J mol}^{-1} \text{ K}^{-1}$$

Note that the energy term in the unit is J, whereas in ΔH it is kJ. This is because the entropy values tend to be smaller and J is more appropriate than kJ. This is an important point which we will come back to in the next section.

Gibbs Standard Free Energy Change $\Delta G°$

A chemical reaction is described as being spontaneous if it tends to occur in the forward direction. An obvious example is burning: petrol will easily burn to form carbon dioxide and water, but turning carbon dioxide and water back into petrol is virtually impossible. An iron nail exposed to a damp atmosphere will tend to rust, but a rusty nail does not 'unrust' without a large input of energy. However, note that 'spontaneous' does not mean that the reaction will happen 'just like that'. Petrol will not burn until the activation energy of a spark or a flame is applied to it. Some reactions which are described as spontaneous will not take place without a lot of energy being supplied.

Both $\Delta H°$ and $\Delta S°$ are taken into account when deciding if a reaction is spontaneous or not. It is known that many exothermic ($\Delta H°$ negative) reactions, such as burning and explosions, are spontaneous. But there are also endothermic reactions where there is an increase in entropy ($\Delta S°$ positive), such as those producing gases from a decomposing solid, which can be spontaneous.

$\Delta H°$, $\Delta S°$ and T are combined to define a new quantity, the Gibbs Free Energy Change, $\Delta G°$ as shown below:

$$\Delta G° = \Delta H° - T\Delta S°$$

where

$\Delta H°$ is the enthalpy change in J mol^{-1} (or kJ mol^{-1}),
T is the temperature in K (degrees Kelvin) (note that 0 °C = 273 K),
$\Delta S°$ is the entropy change in J K^{-1} mol^{-1} (or kJ K^{-1} mol^{-1}).

Note
It is essential that the energy unit of $\Delta H°$ is the same as that of $\Delta S°$; that is, if $\Delta H°$ is expressed in kJ mol^{-1}, $\Delta S°$ must be expressed in kJ K^{-1} mol^{-1}. Or, if $\Delta H°$ is expressed in J mol^{-1}, $\Delta S°$ must be expressed in J K^{-1} mol^{-1}. As noted earlier, $\Delta H°$ values in data books and problems are usually expressed in kJ mol^{-1} and $\Delta S°$ values in J K^{-1} mol^{-1}. If $\Delta H°$ and $\Delta S°$ are expressed with the energy term in kJ, the calculated $\Delta G°$ is in units of kJ mol^{-1}; if these quantities are expressed with the energy term in J, $\Delta G°$ is in units of J mol^{-1}.

A reaction will be spontaneous if $\Delta G°$ is negative and non-spontaneous if $\Delta G°$ is positive.

The four possible situations are summarised in the following table.

$\Delta H°$	$\Delta S°$	$\Delta G°$	Spontaneity of Reaction
−	+	−	Always spontaneous
+	−	+	Always non-spontaneous
+	+	Depends on temperature	At high temperatures spontaneous
−	−	Depends on temperature	At low temperatures spontaneous

Worked Example 12.3

The thermal decomposition of calcium carbonate is given by the equation and data below.

$$CaCO_3(s) \rightarrow CaO(s) + CO_2(g) \qquad \Delta H° = 178 \text{ kJ mol}^{-1}$$
$$\Delta S° = 160 \text{ J K}^{-1} \text{ mol}^{-1}$$

(a)   Calculate $\Delta G°$ at 298 K.

(b)   Over what temperature range will the reaction be spontaneous?

Answer

(a) $\Delta G° = \Delta H° - T\Delta S°$
$$= 178 - 298 \times 0.160$$
$$= 178 - 47.7$$
$$= \textbf{130 kJ mol}^{-1}$$

Note again that the value for $\Delta S°$ was divided by 1000 to convert its energy unit from J to kJ, making it consistent with the energy unit of $\Delta H°$.

(b) $\Delta H°$ has a positive value which would contribute to a non-spontaneous reaction. However, $\Delta S°$ has a positive value, which contributes to a spontaneous reaction. A high temperature will make $-T\Delta S°$ more negative and, above a certain temperature, make $\Delta G°$ negative.

So, *above* this temperature the reaction will be spontaneous. *Below* this temperature, $\Delta G°$ will be *positive* and the reaction will be non-spontaneous. *At exactly this temperature*, $\Delta G° = 0$.

We fit this into the equation:

$$\Delta G^\circ = \Delta H^\circ - T\Delta S^\circ$$

$$0 = \Delta H^\circ - T\Delta S^\circ$$

$$\Delta H^\circ = T\Delta S^\circ$$

$$T = \frac{\Delta H^\circ}{\Delta S^\circ}$$

This last equation, *which only applies when* $\Delta G^\circ = 0$, is worth remembering, rather than having to work it out on every occasion it is required.

Before inserting the data, ΔS° is converted to kJ K^{-1} mol^{-1} to keep the energy units of both ΔH° and ΔS° the same, i.e. kJ.

So $\Delta S^\circ = 160$ J K^{-1} $mol^{-1} = 0.16$ kJ K^{-1} mol^{-1}

Inserting the data into the equation, we have:

$$T = \frac{178}{0.16}$$

$$= \textbf{1110 K}$$

At this temperature, $\Delta G^\circ = 0$. As discussed earlier, above this temperature, ΔG° will be negative and the reaction will be spontaneous.

So the reaction is thermodynamically feasible at temperatures above 1110 K.

Worked Example 12.4

Over what temperature range is the reaction below feasible?

$$2NO + O_2 \rightarrow 2NO_2 \quad \Delta H^\circ = -112 \text{ kJ } mol^{-1}$$
$$\Delta S^\circ = -145 \text{ J } K^{-1} mol^{-1}$$

Answer
Although this problem is essentially the same as Worked Example 12.3, the signs of ΔH° and ΔS° are both negative for this reaction; in Worked Example 12.3, both ΔH° and ΔS° were positive. In this case, ΔH° being negative (exothermic) contributes to a spontaneous reaction; ΔS° being negative contributes to a non-spontaneous reaction. In the equation

$$\Delta G^\circ = \Delta H^\circ - T\Delta S^\circ$$

a low temperature will make $-T\Delta S°$ less negative, making $\Delta G°$ go from being positive to negative with reducing temperature. At a certain temperature, $\Delta G°$ will be 0.

We proceed as before, but going directly to the equation giving the temperature at which $\Delta G° = 0$. Note again that the value for $\Delta S°$ is expressed as -0.145 kJ^{-1} mol^{-1}.

$$T = \frac{\Delta H°}{\Delta S°}$$

$$= \frac{-112}{-0.145}$$

$$= 772 \text{ kJ mol}^{-1}$$

So the reaction is thermodynamically feasible at temperatures below 772 K.

Worked Example 12.5

The dissolving of ammonium nitrate in water is represented by the following equation.

$$NH_4Cl(s) \rightarrow NH_4^+(aq) + Cl^-(aq) \qquad \begin{array}{l} \Delta G° = -6.7 \text{ kJ mol}^{-1} \\ \Delta H° = 16 \text{ kJ mol}^{-1} \end{array}$$

Calculate $\Delta S°$ for the above process at 298 K.

Answer
Rearranging the equation $\Delta G° = \Delta H° - T\Delta S°$, to put $\Delta S°$ on the left, we have:

$$\Delta S° = \frac{\Delta H° - \Delta G°}{T}$$

$$= \frac{16 - (-6.7)}{298}$$

$$= 0.0762 \text{ kJ K}^{-1} \text{ mol}^{-1} \text{ or } 76.2 \text{ J K}^{-1} \text{ mol}^{-1}$$

PROBLEMS

1   The thermal decomposition of barium carbonate is represented by the following equation.

$$BaCO_3(s) \rightarrow BaO(s) + CO_2(g)$$

Substance	ΔH°_f/kJ mol^{-1}	S°/J K^{-1} mol^{-1}
$BaCO_3(s)$	−1213	112
$BaO(s)$	−548	70
$CO_2(g)$	−394	214

(a) Calculate ΔH° and ΔS° for the above reaction.

(b) Calculate ΔG° for the reaction at 300 K.

(c) Over what temperature range will the decomposition of barium carbonate be spontaneous?

2
$$2Al(OH)_3(s) \rightarrow Al_2O_3(s) + 3H_2O(g)$$

Substance	ΔH°_f/kJ mol^{-1}	S°/J K^{-1} mol^{-1}
$Al(OH)_3(s)$	−1284	71
$Al_2O_3(s)$	−1676	51
$H_2O(g)$	−242	189

(a) Calculate ΔH° and ΔS° for the above reaction.

(b) Calculate ΔG° (per mole of equation as above) for the reaction at 500 K.

(c) Over what temperature range will the reaction be spontaneous?

3 Ammonium chloride can decompose to form ammonia and hydrogen chloride gases as shown by the equation below.

$$NH_4Cl(s) \rightarrow NH_3(g) + HCl(g)$$

The relevant thermodynamic data is given in the table.

Substance	ΔH°_f/kJ mol^{-1}	S°/J K^{-1} mol^{-1}
$NH_4Cl(s)$	−315	95
$NH_3(g)$	−46	193
$HCl(g)$	−93	187

(a) Calculate $\Delta H°$ and $\Delta S°$ for this reaction.

(b) Calculate $\Delta G°$ for the reaction at 1000k.

(c) Over what temperature range is the reaction spontaneous?

4   The industrial production of ammonia by the Haber Process is represented by the following equation.

$$N_2(g) \ + \ 3H_2(g) \ \rightarrow \ 2NH_3(g)$$

The relevant data are given below.

Substance	$\Delta H°_f$/kJ mol^{-1}	$S°$/J K^{-1} mol^{-1}
$N_2(g)$	0	192
$H_2(g)$	0	131
$NH_3(g)$	-46	193

(a) Calculate $\Delta H°$ and $\Delta S°$ (per mole of $N_2(g)$) for this reaction.

(b) Calculate $\Delta G°$ (per mole of $N_2(g)$) for the reaction at 500 K.

(c) Over what temperature range is the reaction spontaneous?

5   Consider the equation and table of thermodynamic data below.

$$2ZnS(s) \ + \ 3O_2(g) \ \rightarrow \ 2ZnO(s) \ + \ 2SO_2(g)$$

Substance	$\Delta H°_f$/kJ mol^{-1}	$S°$/J K^{-1} mol^{-1}
$ZnS(s)$	-206	58
$O_2(g)$	0	205
$ZnO(s)$	-350	44
$SO_2(g)$	-297	248

(a) Calculate $\Delta H°$ and $\Delta S°$ (per mole of equation as above) for this reaction.

(b) Calculate $\Delta G°$ (per mole of equation as above) for the reaction at 600 K.

(c) Over what temperature range is the reaction spontaneous?

6   The equation and data below relate to the decomposition of sodium hydrogencarbonate.

$$2NaHCO_3(s) \rightarrow Na_2CO_3(s) + H_2O(g) + CO_2(g)$$

Substance	$\Delta H°_f$/kJ mol^{-1}	$S°$/J K^{-1} mol^{-1}
$NaHCO_3(s)$	-951	102
$Na_2CO_3(s)$	-1131	135
$H_2O(g)$	-242	189
$CO_2(g)$	-394	214

(a) Calculate $\Delta H°$ and $\Delta S°$ (per mole of equation as above) for this reaction.

(b) Calculate $\Delta G°$ for the reaction at 600 K.

(c) Over what temperature range is the reaction spontaneous?

7   An important reaction in the Ostwald Processs, the industrial production of sulphuric acid, is shown by the equation below in which sulphur dioxide is oxidised to sulphur trioxide.

$$SO_2(g) + \tfrac{1}{2}O_2(g) \rightarrow SO_3(g)$$

Substance	$\Delta H°_f$/kJ mol^{-1}	$S°$/J K^{-1} mol^{-1}
$SO_2(g)$	-297	248
$O_2(g)$	0	205
$SO_3(g)$	-396	257

(a) Calculate $\Delta H°$ and $\Delta S°$ (per mole of $SO_2(g)$ reacted) for this reaction.

(b) Calculate $\Delta G°$ for the reaction at 298 K.

(c) Over what temperature range is the reaction spontaneous?

8   The equation below shows the reaction of nitrogen monoxide to form nitrous oxide and oxygen.

$$4NO(g) \rightarrow 2N_2O(g) + O_2(g)$$

Substance	$\Delta H°_f$/kJ mol^{-1}	$S°$/J K^{-1} mol^{-1}
NO(g)	91	211
N_2O(g)	82	222
O_2(g)	0	205

(a) Calculate $\Delta H°$ and $\Delta S°$ (per mole of equation as above) for this reaction.

(b) Calculate $\Delta G°$ for the reaction at 300 K.

(c) Over what temperature range is the reaction spontaneous?

9   Hydrogen chloride can undergo an addition reaction with ethyne as shown below.

$$C_2H_2(g) + 2HCl(g) \rightarrow CH_2ClCH_2Cl(l)$$

Substance	$\Delta H°_f$/kJ mol^{-1}	$S°$/J K^{-1} mol^{-1}
C_2H_2(g)	227	201
HCl(g)	−92	187
CH_2ClCH_2Cl(l)	−166	208

(a) Calculate $\Delta H°$ and $\Delta S°$ (per mole of C_2H_2(g)) for the reaction given.

(b) Over what temperature range is this reaction thermodynamically feasible?

10 $$2NaCl(s) + CaCO_3(s) \rightarrow CaCl_2(s) + Na_2CO_3(s)$$

Substance	$\Delta H°_f$/kJ mol^{-1}	$S°$/J K^{-1} mol^{-1}
NaCl(s)	−411	72
$CaCO_3$(s)	−1208	92
$CaCl_2$(s)	−795	108
Na_2CO_3(g)	−1131	135

(a) Calculate $\Delta H°$ and $\Delta S°$ (per mole of equation as above) for this reaction.

(b) Calculate $\Delta G°$ for the reaction at 298 K.

(c) Over what temperature range is the reaction spontaneous?

Electrochemical Cells

Calculating the Electromotive Force (emf) of a Cell

An electrochemical cell is an example of a spontaneous redox (reduction/oxidation) reaction which is put to work in 'batteries' producing electricity to operate torches, radios, etc. A simple example of an electrochemical cell is shown below.

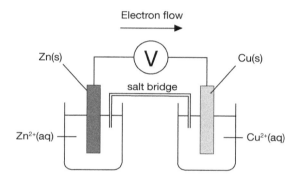

Zinc is more reactive than copper, which means that zinc undergoes oxidation more readily than copper. The zinc reacts as follows:

$$Zn(s) \rightarrow Zn^{2+}(aq) + 2e^-$$

Electrons produced flow through the wire to the copper electrode where copper(II) ions from the solution surrounding the electrode undergo the reduction reaction below:

$$Cu^{2+}(aq) + 2e^- \rightarrow Cu(s)$$

The two ion–electron equations taking place in a cell are often described as **half-reactions** because each describes half of the overall redox reaction taking place.

The circuit is completed by ions moving through the solution in the salt bridge.

As this cell operates, the zinc electrode gradually dissolves into the solution and the concentration of copper(II) ions in the right-hand solution decreases. This latter change could be observed by the blue colour of the copper(II) solution becoming paler. At some point, one or other of the substances involved will 'run out' and the electron flow will stop. This is exactly what happens when a 'battery' (usually more correctly called a cell) stops working.

Rather than needing a picture to describe a cell as shown above, there is an internationally accepted short form. The cell above would be described as:

$$Zn(s) \mid Zn^{2+}(aq) \parallel Cu^{2+}(aq) \mid Cu(s)$$

The left-hand side is where the oxidation takes place. This is the negative electrode, since it is at this electrode that the electrons get produced. The right-hand side is where reduction takes place at the positive electrode. The single vertical lines separate the metal electrode from its ions; the double lines represent the salt bridge.

Different oxidation and reduction reactions have different tendencies to take place, ranging from those tending to happen with a very strong 'push' to those with practically no 'push' at all.

For example, we know that a very reactive metal such as sodium will react very quickly with oxygen or water. The oxidation of the sodium is shown by the following equation:

$$Na(s) \rightarrow Na^{+}(aq) + e^{-}$$

This reaction can be described as having a *very strong tendency* to take place.

In contrast, silver is an example of a very unreactive metal which could be left in water for weeks and still keep the shininess of the pure metal. It has an *extremely weak tendency* to undergo the oxidation below.

$$Ag(s) \rightarrow Ag^{+}(aq) + e^{-}$$

The tendencies of ion–electron reactions to take place have been measured numerically by carrying them out in electrochemical cells where one of the electrodes is known as a hydrogen electrode, as shown in the following diagram.

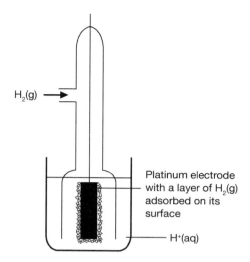

This is a platinum electrode, which has a surface that can allow hydrogen gas to 'adsorb' ('stick') to its surface. Hydrogen gas is fed into the glass container to keep hydrogen on the electrode as it operates. The platinum is in a solution of acid, $H^+(aq)$. This creates a 'rod' of hydrogen in a solution of hydrogen ions, similar to the zinc or copper electrodes in solutions of their own ions, considered earlier.

Using this electrode coupled in a cell with other substances undergoing oxidations or reductions, and measuring the voltage of the cells, a measure of the 'electrical push', known as the **electromotive force (emf)**, can be obtained for a whole range of reactions. The symbol for emf when obtained under standard conditions of temperature, concentration and pressure is $E°$; the unit is the volt, symbol V.

Page 11 of the Data Book lists a range of reactions, all expressed as reductions, with their emf values compared with a hydrogen electrode under standard conditions. The table is entitled 'Electrochemical Series: Standard Reduction Potentials'. With reference to this series, note the following points: the $E°$ value for the reduction of $H^+(aq)$ is given the value 0.00 V. All other reactions and $E°$ values are compared with this.

The most likely reductions are at the bottom of the table; the least likely at the top. The more positive the $E°$ value the more electrical 'push' the reaction has; reactions with negative $E°$ values have got less 'push' or tendency to take place.

The use of the Electrochemical Series and the $E°$ values can be seen in the following Worked Examples.

Worked Example 13.1

Consider the cell pictured below.

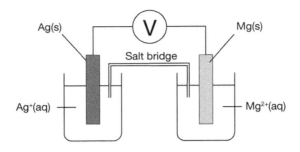

(a) Write the ion–electron equations describing the electrode reactions.

(b) Calculate the emf of the cell, assuming standard conditions.

Answer

(a) We have to decide which oxidation and which reduction will take place at the electrodes. There are two choices; either

$$Mg(s) \rightarrow Mg^{2+}(aq) + 2e^- \qquad E° = 2.37 \text{ V}$$
$$Ag^+(aq) + e^- \rightarrow Ag(s) \qquad E° = 0.80 \text{ V}$$

or

$$Mg^{2+}(aq) + 2e^- \rightarrow Mg(s) \qquad E° = -2.37 \text{ V}$$
$$Ag(s) \rightarrow Ag^+(aq) + e^- \qquad E° = -0.80 \text{ V}$$

For a cell to operate spontaneously, that is, without any outside energy added, the combined $E°$ values have to add up to a *positive value* to give a positive 'push' or driving force for the overall cell reaction.

The $E°$ values of the former pair of reactions add to give an overall *positive value*; so they will take place. The second pair of reactions give an overall *negative value* and so will not take place.

(b) Each electrode potential is a measure of the 'push' of the half-reaction to take place and so the oxidation and reduction potentials *added together* give a measure of the total 'driving force' of the cell.

So the emf of this cell is 2.37 + 0.80 = **3.17 V**.

Note

Looking back at the selected ion–electron equations we see that the oxidation equation involves a loss of two electrons, and the reduction involves a gain of one electron. It might seem obvious that we ought to balance these equations by mutiplying the reduction equation by 2. We might therefore think that the $E°$ value of 0.80 for the reduction of $Ag^+(aq)$ should be multiplied by 2 before being added to the oxidation $E°$ in the final calculation. *However, that is not the case.* An $E°$ value is a measure of the *tendency* for the reaction to take place; the number of electrons in either of the ion–electron equations involved does *not* affect the $E°$ and, therefore, the overall emf for the cell. It is, however, the case that if we wanted to obtain the *overall redox reaction* taking place we would have to balance the electrons and combine the equations as below.

$$Mg(s) \rightarrow Mg^{2+}(aq) + 2e^-$$
$$2 \times [Ag^+(aq) + e^- \rightarrow Ag(s)]$$

When the reduction is multiplied by 2 we have

$$Mg(s) \rightarrow Mg^{2+}(aq) + 2e^-$$
$$2Ag^+(aq) + 2e^- \rightarrow 2Ag(s)$$

When added together the two electrons on each side of the overall equation cancel out and we have:

$$Mg(s) + 2Ag^+(aq) \rightarrow Mg^{2+}(aq) + 2Ag(s)$$

Worked Example 13.2

Consider the electrochemical cell below.

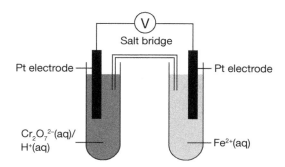

(a) Obtain the ion–electron equations for the electrode reactions.

(b) Calculate the emf of the cell under standard conditions.

Answer

(a) The only difference from the previous Worked Example is that neither electrode takes part in the cell reaction. Platinum is used here precisely because it is so unreactive that the only substances taking part are in the solutions.

The left-hand solution contains dichromate ions in acid solution. This is a common oxidising agent which should be familiar from the Higher course. There is only one possible equation in the Data Book. The equation and $E°$ value are given below.

$$Cr_2O_7^{2-}(aq) + 14H^+(aq) + 6e^- \rightarrow 2Cr^{3+}(aq) + 7H_2O(l) \qquad E° = 1.33 \text{ V}$$

At this point it is worth noting the reason why the left-hand electrode was described as containing $Cr_2O_7^{2-}(aq)$ *and* $H^+(aq)$. The reason for the presence of the $H^+(aq)$ can be explained by looking at the above equation; every dichromate ion needs 14 hydrogen ions for the reduction to take place. (The solution is often described as acidified dichromate solution for this reason.)

We now look at the right-hand solution, which is $Fe^{2+}(aq)$. We need to find an oxidation reaction that starts with $Fe^{2+}(aq)$ and has an $E°$ value which, when added to the 1.33 V of the above reduction, gives an overall positive emf. Looking at the right-hand side of the Electrochemical Series there is only one oxidation starting with $Fe^{2+}(aq)$. Its equation and $E°$ value are given below.

$$Fe^{2+}(aq) \rightarrow Fe^{3+}(aq) + e^- \qquad E° = -0.77 \text{ V}$$

(b) This $E°$ value, when added to the $E°$ for the reduction, gives the overall emf for the cell as below.

$$emf = 1.33 + (-0.77) = 0.56 \text{ V}$$

Note

One of the reasons why this cell was chosen as a Worked Example is because there are three ion–electron equations involving iron or iron ions on page 11 of the Data Book. They are noted below.

$$Fe^{2+}(aq) + 2e^- \rightarrow Fe(s) \qquad E° = -0.44 \text{ V}$$
$$Fe^{3+}(aq) + 3e^- \rightarrow Fe(s) \qquad E° = -0.04 \text{ V}$$
$$Fe^{3+}(aq) + e^- \rightarrow Fe^{2+}(aq) \qquad E° = 0.77 \text{ V}$$

It is very easy (and not uncommon) for students to make a mistake in selecting the correct equation and $E°$ value in a cell reaction involving iron or iron ions. It is essential to check that the right *type* of reaction (oxidation or reduction) is selected and to make sure that the overall emf calculated is a *positive* value.

Calculating $\Delta G°$ from Electromotive Force (emf) Values

Since the emf is a measure of the 'push' or tendency of the overall reaction to take place, it should come as no surprise to learn that the emf, $E°$, of a cell is related to the $\Delta G°$ which gives a measure of how spontaneous (or otherwise) a reaction is. The mathematical relationship is shown below.

$$\Delta G° = -nFE°$$

- n is the number of moles of electrons transferred 'per mole of the chemical equation as written'. In the case of the cell considered in Worked Example 13.1, where the overall reaction is

$$Zn(s) + Cu^{2+}(aq) \rightarrow Zn^{2+}(aq) + Cu(s)$$

 $n = 2$ since 2 mol of electrons have been transferred from 1 mol of Zn to 1 mol of Cu^{2+}. Refer to Worked Example 13.1 if this is not clear.

- F is the Faraday constant = 9.65×10^4 C mol^{-1} (Coulombs per mol of electrons). This value is given on page 19 of the Data Book.

- $E°$ is the emf if a redox reaction had been carried out in an electrochemical cell under standard conditions.

$\Delta G°$ has the unit of J mol^{-1}, although quantities are more usually expressed in kJ mol^{-1}. If required, this conversion can take place at the end of the calculation by dividing by 1000. Alternatively, the equation below can be used in the first place:

$$\Delta G° = -96.5nE°$$

This gives $\Delta G°$ in units of kJ mol^{-1} directly by including the value of the Faraday divided by 1000.

Note
Observant students may be concerned that the units on the left- and right-hand sides of the equation do not appear to work out to be the same. On the left we have J mol^{-1} (or kJ mol^{-1}) and on the right we have coulombs and volts. The explanation lies in the definition of the volt: a volt is a joule per coulomb (J C^{-1}), which means that the units on the left- and the right-hand sides of the equation *are* the same.

Worked Example 13.3

Consider the cell described by the standard international form below.

$$Zn(s) \mid Zn^{2+}(aq) \parallel Ag^+(aq) \mid Ag(s)$$

(a) Write the ion–electron equations for the cell reactions.

(b) Calculate the emf of the cell under standard conditions.

(c) Calculate ΔG°, per mole of Zn, for the cell reaction

Answer

(a) The left-hand side of the above cell shows the substances involved in the oxidation. So the oxidation must be:

$$Zn(s) \rightarrow Zn^{2+}(aq) + 2e^- \qquad E^\circ = 0.76 \text{ V}$$

The reduction must be:

$$Ag^+(aq) + e^- \rightarrow Ag(s) \qquad E^\circ = 0.80 \text{ V}$$

(b) The emf is simply the sum of the reduction and oxidation E° values. So:

$$\text{emf} = 0.76 + 0.80 = \textbf{1.56 V}$$

(c) $\Delta G^\circ = -nFE^\circ$
E° has been calculated at (b) above to be 1.56 V.
$F = 9.65 \times 10^4 \text{ C mol}^{-1}$.
$n = 2$ for the overall equation $Zn(s) + 2Ag^+(aq) \rightarrow Zn^{2+}(aq) + 2Ag(s)$ since 2 mol of electrons would be transferred for every 1 mol of $Zn(s)$ oxidised and every 2 mol of $Ag^+(aq)$ reduced. ΔG° is calculated as follows

$$\begin{aligned} \Delta G^\circ &= -2 \times 9.65 \times 10^4 \times 1.56 \\ &= -3.01 \times 10^5 \text{ J mol}^{-1} \\ &= \textbf{-301 kJ mol}^{-1} \end{aligned}$$

Alternatively:
$$\begin{aligned} \Delta G^\circ &= -96.5nE^\circ \\ &= -96.5 \times 2 \times 1.56 \\ &= \textbf{-301 kJ mol}^{-1} \end{aligned}$$

PROBLEMS

1   Consider the cell shown below.

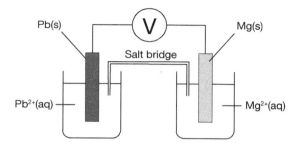

(a) Obtain the ion–electron equations for the electrode reactions.

(b) Write the equation for the overall cell reaction.

(c) Calculate the emf of the cell under standard conditions.

(d) Calculate the $\Delta G°$ for the overall cell reaction, per mole of equation as at part (b).

2   Consider the cell pictured below.

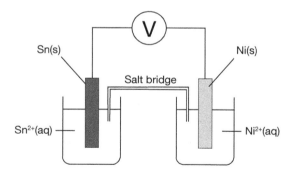

(a) Obtain the ion–electron equations for the electrode reactions.

(b) Write the equation for the overall cell reaction.

(c) Calculate the emf of the cell under standard conditions.

(d) Calculate the $\Delta G°$ for the overall cell reaction, per mole of equation as at part (b).

3   Consider the cell pictured below.

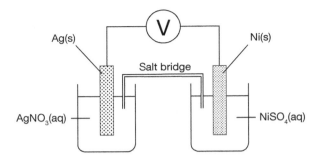

(a)   Obtain the ion–electron equations for the electrode reactions.

(b)   Write the equation for the overall cell reaction.

(c)   Calculate the emf of the cell under standard conditions.

(d)   Calculate the $\Delta G°$ for the overall cell reaction, per mole of equation as at part (b).

4   A torch 'battery', more correctly known as a dry cell, is shown below

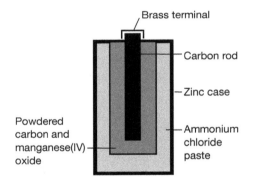

The cell reactions are as follows:

$$Zn(s) \rightarrow Zn^{2+}(aq) + 2e^- \qquad\qquad E° = +0.76 \text{ V}$$
$$2NH_4^+(aq) + 2e^- \rightarrow 2NH_3(g) + H_2(g) \qquad E° = +0.74 \text{ V}$$

(a)   What is the emf of a dry cell under standard conditions?

(b)   Calculate $\Delta G°$ (per mole of Zn) for the overall cell reaction.

5   Consider the cell pictured below.

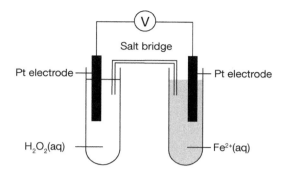

The standard reduction potential for the reaction

$$H_2O_2(aq) + 2H^+(aq) + 2e^- \rightarrow 2H_2O(l)$$

is 1.77 V.

(a) Write the equation for the balanced redox reaction taking place in the cell.

(b) Calculate the emf of the cell under standard conditions.

(c) Calculate the $\Delta G°$ (per mole of $H_2O_2(aq)$) for the overall cell reaction.

6   Consider the cell pictured below.

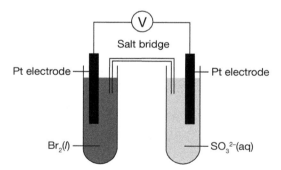

(a) Obtain the ion–electron equations for the electrode reactions.

(b) Write the equation for the overall cell reaction.

(c) Calculate the emf of the cell under standard conditions.

(d) Calculate the $\Delta G°$ (per mole of $Br_2(l)$) for the overall cell reaction.

7   Consider the cell pictured below in which magnesium is coupled to an unknown metal M in a solution of its ions. The cell emf is 1.63 V under standard conditions. The direction of electron flow in the external circuit is shown.

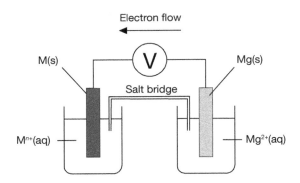

Electron flow

M(s)   V   Mg(s)

Salt bridge

M^{n+}(aq) Mg^{2+}(aq)

(a) Calculate the standard reduction potential for the reaction:

$$M^{n+}(aq) + ne^- \rightarrow M(s)$$

(b) Identify metal M from the Data Book.

(c) Write the overall redox equation for the cell reaction.

(d) Calculate $\Delta G°$ per mole of equation as written in the answer to part (c) above.

8   In a lead–acid car battery, the cells are charged by electrical energy being supplied from an external power source (a charger) to cause the reactions below to take place in each cell of the battery.

$PbSO_4(s) + 2e \rightarrow Pb(s) + SO_4^{2-}(aq)$ $E° = -0.36$ V
$PbSO_4(aq) + 2H_2O(l) \rightarrow PbO_2(s) + 4H^+(aq) + SO_4^{2-}(aq) + 2e$ $E° = -1.69$ V

(a) When the battery is being used as a power source, the battery discharges and the opposite reactions to those given above take place at the electrodes. Use the data given to calculate the emf of one of the cells of the battery, assuming standard conditions.

(b) Calculate the $\Delta G°$, per mole of Pb reacted, for the cell reaction when a cell discharges, assuming standard conditions.

9   The diagram below shows a simplified picture of an alkaline 'fuel cell' where hydrogen is used as a fuel but, instead of being burned to produce heat, it is used in an electrochemical cell to produce an electrical current.

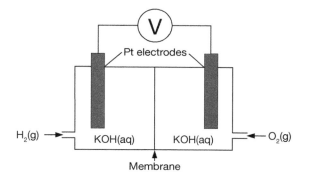

At the left-hand electrode, oxidation takes place in which hydrogen gas reacts with hydroxide ions from the potassium hydroxide electrolyte. At the right-hand electrode, reduction takes place in which oxygen gas reacts with water. The membrane is a thin sheet of material which separates the two sides of the cell, but it contains tiny pores which allow ions to flow through under electrical pressure. This serves the same function as a salt bridge.

(a) Obtain the equations for the reduction and oxidation reactions from the Data Book.

(b) Balance these equations to obtain the overall cell reaction

(b) Calculate the cell voltage, assuming standard conditions apply.

(c) Calculate $\Delta G°$ per mole of $H_2(g)$ reacted.

10   The equation below represents the redox reaction taking place in a cell.

$$Cu(s) + 2Ag^+(aq) \rightarrow Cu^{2+}(aq) + 2Ag(s)$$

(a) Calculate the emf of the cell under standard conditions.

(b) Calculate $\Delta G°$, per mole of $Cu(s)$, for the above reaction.

(c) When the above reaction is carried out in a calorimeter (to measure the heat produced), it is found that the $\Delta H°$ for the reaction is -121 kJ mol^{-1} (i.e. 121 kJ per mole of the above reaction as written in the equation). Use this value, and that for $\Delta G°$ calculated at (b) above, to calculate $\Delta S°$ for the reaction, again assuming standard conditions, including at a temperature of 298 K.

Rate Equations

For a reaction described by the equation below

$$aA + bB + cC \rightarrow \text{products,}$$

the rate equation (or rate law) can be written as

$$\text{rate} = k[A]^x[B]^y[C]^z$$

where k is the **rate constant** and x, y and z are integers, usually small numbers such as 0, 1, 2 or 3. Note that the symbol for rate constant is k, not K, which is the equilibrium constant.

In this equation, x is the order of reaction with respect to substance A, y is the order of reaction with respect to substance B, etc. The overall order of reaction is given by $x + y + z$.

Note that the powers x, y and z to which the concentrations are raised in the rate equation generally bear no relation to the numbers of moles of the substances in the balanced equation. *It is not possible to work out the rate equation from the balanced equation. The rate equation can only be obtained by experiment.*

The rate equation can be worked out by carrying out the reaction several times, altering (usually doubling) the concentration of one reactant at a time, keeping all others constant. The amount of product obtained after a short time gives a measure of the initial rate of reaction. This can be seen in the following Worked Example and the related Problems at the end of the chapter.

Worked Example 14.1

Consider the table of data showing how the initial rate of reaction between substances A, B and C is affected by changing their concentrations at constant temperature.

Experiment Number	Initial concentration of A / mol l⁻¹	Initial concentration of B / mol l⁻¹	Initial concentration of C / mol l⁻¹	Initial rate of reaction / mol l⁻¹ s⁻¹
1	0.1	0.1	0.1	0.05
2	0.2	0.1	0.1	0.10
3	0.1	0.2	0.1	0.05
4	0.1	0.1	0.2	0.20

Obtain the rate equation for the above reaction, giving the correct unit.

Answer
We analyse the data by comparing experiments where the concentration of one reactant is doubled while the others remain the same.

- Comparing experiments 1 and 2, doubling [A] doubles the rate. This means that the order of reaction with respect to A is **1**.

- Comparing experiments 1 and 3, doubling [B] has no effect on the rate. This means that the order of reaction with respect to B is **0**.

- Comparing experiments 1 and 4, doubling [C] multiplies the rate by 4. This means that the order of reaction with respect to C is **2**.

These results tell us that the rate equation must be:

$$\text{rate} = k[A]^1[B]^0[C]^2$$

or, more simply

$$\text{rate} = k[A][C]^2$$

([B] disappears from the equation because *any* number to the power 0 has the value 1.)

The overall order of reaction is therefore 3; that is, it is a 3rd order reaction.

The value for the rate constant is obtained by putting in the values for concentrations and rate for *any one* of the experiments. (Since the experiments are all carried out at the same temperature, and the rate constant *is a constant* under these conditions, the data for all four experiments will give the same value for k.)

Taking the results for experiment 1, we have:

$$\text{rate} = k[A][C]^2$$
$$0.05 = k \times 0.1 \times (0.1)^2$$
$$0.05 = k \times 0.001$$
$$50 = k$$

So the rate constant, k, has the numerical value of 50.

The unit of k is obtained by inserting the units of rate and concentration into the equation and solving for k. It is useful to use c as shorthand for the unit of concentration, mol l^{-1}, and therefore c s^{-1} as shorthand for the unit of rate, mol l^{-1} s^{-1}.

$$\text{rate} = k[A][C]^2$$
$$c\,s^{-1} = k\,c\,c^2$$
$$c\,s^{-1} = k\,c^3$$
$$\frac{c\,s^{-1}}{c^3} = k$$
$$c\,s^{-1}c^{-3} = k$$
$$c^{-2}\,s^{-1} = k$$

At this stage, we substitute c for the full unit of mol l^{-1}. Note that c^{-1} would therefore be mol^{-1} l, so c^{-2} would be mol^{-2} l^2. So the above equation becomes

$$\text{mol}^{-2}\,l^2\,s^{-1} = k$$

So the unit of the rate constant in this case is **mol^{-2} l^2 s^{-1}**.

If students find this over complicated, they may prefer to learn the rate constant units for the most likely rate equations to appear in the examination. These are:

1st order:	s^{-1}	(or min^{-1})
2nd order:	mol^{-1} l s^{-1}	(or mol^{-1} l min^{-1})
3rd order:	mol^{-2} l^2 s^{-1}	(or mol^{-2} l^2 min^{-1})

PROBLEMS

1   The following table shows how the rate of reaction between substances A and B varies as their concentrations are changed.

Experiment Number	Initial concentration of A / mol l^{-1}	Initial concentration of B / mol l^{-1}	Initial rate of reaction / mol l^{-1} s^{-1}
1	1	1	0.1
2	2	1	0.2
3	2	2	0.2

(a) Obtain the rate law for the reaction.

(b) Calculate the rate constant, with appropriate unit, for the reaction under the above conditions.

2 The table below shows how the rate of reaction between substances X and Y varies as their concentrations are changed.

Experiment Number	Initial concentration of X / mol l^{-1}	Initial concentration of Y / mol l^{-1}	Initial rate of reaction / mol l^{-1} min^{-1}
1	1	1	0.2
2	2	1	0.4
3	1	2	0.4

(a) Obtain the rate law for the reaction.

(b) Calculate the rate constant, with appropriate unit, for the reaction under the above conditions.

3 The table below shows how the rate of reaction between substances A and B varies as their concentrations are changed.

Experiment Number	Initial concentration of A / mol l^{-1}	Initial concentration of B / mol l^{-1}	Initial rate of reaction / mol l^{-1} s^{-1}
1	0.1	0.1	0.02
2	0.1	0.2	0.08
3	0.2	0.1	0.02

(a) Obtain the rate law for the reaction.

(b) Calculate the rate constant, with appropriate unit, for the reaction under the above conditions.

4   The table below shows how the rate of reaction between substances X, Y and Z varies as their concentrations are changed.

Experiment Number	Initial concentration of X / mol l⁻¹	Initial concentration of Y / mol l⁻¹	Initial concentration of Z / mol l⁻¹	Initial rate of reaction / mol l⁻¹ min⁻¹
1	0.2	0.2	0.2	0.004
2	0.4	0.2	0.2	0.016
3	0.4	0.4	0.2	0.032
4	0.2	0.2	0.4	0.004

(a) Obtain the rate law for the reaction.

(b) Calculate the rate constant, with appropriate unit, for the reaction under the above conditions.

5   The table below shows how the rate of reaction between substances X, Y and Z varies as their concentrations are changed.

Experiment Number	Initial concentration of X / mol l⁻¹	Initial concentration of Y / mol l⁻¹	Initial concentration of Z / mol l⁻¹	Initial rate of reaction / mol l⁻¹ min⁻¹
1	0.3	0.3	0.3	0.054
2	0.3	0.6	0.3	0.216
3	0.6	0.6	0.3	0.216
4	0.3	0.3	0.6	0.108

(a) Obtain the rate law for the reaction.

(b) Calculate the rate constant, with appropriate unit, for the reaction under the above conditions.

6 The table below shows how the rate of reaction between substances X, Y and Z varies as their concentrations are changed.

Experiment Number	Initial concentration of X / mol l⁻¹	Initial concentration of Y / mol l⁻¹	Initial concentration of Z / mol l⁻¹	Initial rate of reaction / mol l⁻¹ s⁻¹
1	0.05	0.05	0.05	0.02
2	0.10	0.10	0.05	0.08
3	0.10	0.05	0.05	0.04
4	0.10	0.10	0.10	0.08

(a) Obtain the rate law for the reaction.

(b) Calculate the rate constant, with appropriate unit, for the reaction under the above conditions.

7 The table below shows how the rate of reaction between substances A, B and C varies as their concentrations are changed.

Experiment Number	Initial concentration of A / mol l⁻¹	Initial concentration of B / mol l⁻¹	Initial concentration of C / mol l⁻¹	Initial rate of reaction / mol l⁻¹ min⁻¹
1	0.015	0.02	0.015	0.0045
2	0.03	0.04	0.03	0.0180
3	0.015	0.02	0.03	0.0090
4	0.03	0.02	0.03	0.0180

(a) Obtain the rate law for the reaction.

(b) Calculate the rate constant, with appropriate unit, for the reaction under the above conditions.

8   The table below shows how the rate of reaction between solutions of substances X, Y and Z varies as their concentrations are changed.

Experiment Number	Initial concentration of X / mol l^{-1}	Initial concentration of Y / mol l^{-1}	Initial concentration of Z / mol l^{-1}	Initial rate of reaction / mol l^{-1} min^{-1}
1	0.015	0.02	0.05	0.0030
2	0.030	0.04	0.05	0.012
3	0.030	0.02	0.05	0.0030
4	0.015	0.02	0.10	0.0060

(a) Obtain the rate law for the reaction.

(b) Calculate the rate constant, with appropriate unit, for the reaction under the above conditions.

9   The table below shows how the rate of reaction between solutions of substances X, Y and Z varies as their concentrations are changed.

Experiment Number	Initial concentration of X / mol l^{-1}	Initial concentration of Y / mol l^{-1}	Initial concentration of Z / mol l^{-1}	Initial rate of reaction / mol l^{-1} s^{-1}
1	0.20	0.20	0.20	0.015
2	0.40	0.20	0.40	0.060
3	0.40	0.40	0.40	0.060
4	0.40	0.20	0.20	0.030

(a) Obtain the rate law for the reaction.

(b) Calculate the rate constant, with appropriate unit, for the reaction under the above conditions.

10 The table below shows how the rate of reaction between substances A, B and C varies as their concentrations are changed.

Experiment Number	Initial concentration of A / mol l^{-1}	Initial concentration of B / mol l^{-1}	Initial concentration of C / mol l^{-1}	Initial rate of reaction / mol l^{-1} s^{-1}
1	0.01	0.005	0.02	0.0012
2	0.01	0.01	0.02	0.0048
3	0.02	0.005	0.02	0.0012
4	0.01	0.01	0.04	0.0048

(a) Obtain the rate law for the reaction.

(b) Calculate the rate constant, with appropriate unit, for the reaction under the above conditions.

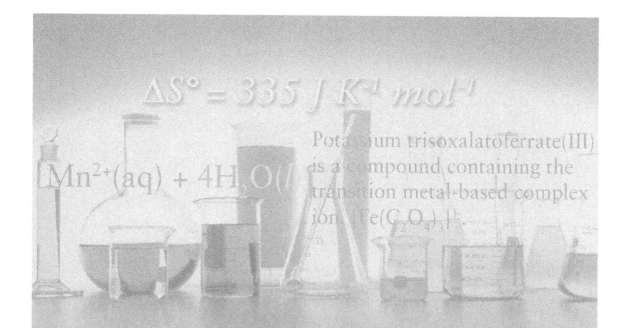

Part Two

Prescribed Practical Activities

Preparation of Potassium Trisoxalatoferrate(III)

Potassium trisoxalatoferrate(III) is a compound containing the transition metal-based complex ion, $[Fe(C_2O_4)_3]^{3-}$. The $C_2O_4^{2-}$ is the **oxalate ion** – a **bidentate** ('two-toothed') ligand, containing two lone pairs of electrons capable of binding to the Fe^{3+} ion. The structure of the oxalate ion is shown below. You need not learn this but you should be able to recognise it.

Three oxalate ions provide a total of six lone pairs of electrons which bind to each Fe^{3+} in an octahedral arrangement.

In simplified form, the preparation of the final product $K_3[Fe(C_2O_4)_3].3H_2O$ involves an iron(III) compound reacted with oxalate ions.

If the mass of the original iron(III) compound is known, and the other reactants are in excess, the percentage yield of product can be easily calculated. Each mole of the iron in the original compound will theoretically produce 1 mole of the final compound because the latter contains 1 mole of Fe per mole of the compound. (Check with the formula above.) So if there were a 100% yield (which there will not be), 1 mole of the original iron(III) compound would produce 1 mole of hydrated potassium trisoxalatoferrate(III).

The percentage yield is calculated by:

$$\frac{actual \text{ mass of product} \times 100}{theoretical \text{ mass of product}} \%$$

PROBLEM

A sample of hydrated potassium trisoxalatoferrate(III), formula $K_3[Fe(C_2O_4)_3].3H_2O$, was made by reacting 5.23 g of ammonium iron(II) sulphate-6-water, formula $(NH_4)_2Fe(SO_4)_2.6H_2O$ with an excess of oxalic acid and other reagents. The mass of the final product was 5.91 g. Calculate the percentage yield of product by mass.

Colorimetric Determination of Manganese in Steel

Colorimetry is a method of measuring the concentration of a coloured compound by passing coloured light through it and measuring how much of the light is absorbed by the solution (the absorbance) or how much is allowed to get through the solution (the transmittance). The more concentrated the solution, the deeper the colour will be and the more light will be absorbed (and the less light will get through). A simplified picture of a colorimeter is shown below.

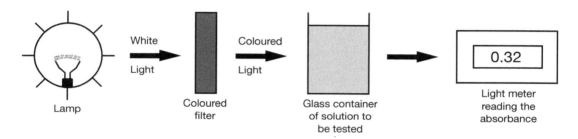

Lamp — White Light — Coloured filter — Coloured Light — Glass container of solution to be tested — 0.32 Light meter reading the absorbance

A beam of white light is shone through a coloured filter to give a chosen colour of light. The colour of light chosen is that which will be most absorbed by the colour of the solution. For example, the solution whose concentration to be measured in this case is light purple/pink; green light is most absorbed by purple, so a green filter is used. This is then shone through a solution of the coloured compound and the intensity of the light coming through the solution is measured by a light meter. To discount any absorbance caused by the water (or other solvent) or the glass container, the light beam is split into two parts, one going through the test sample and the other going through an identical container containing only the pure solvent. The absorbance caused by the latter (known as a 'blank') is subtracted from the test sample reading.

A more sophisticated version of the colorimeter is a spectrophotometer, where specific wavelengths can be selected, rather than broad bands of colour. In an analysis of a coloured compound the absorbance of the coloured solution would be measured over the whole visible spectrum from about 400 nm to 700 nm. (See page 14 of the Data Book for colours and their wavelengths.) The wavelength at which most absorbance takes place is noted. The spectrophotometer would then be set to that wavelength and the analysis carried out as with the colorimeter.

A series of known concentrations of the solution is made up and the amount of absorbance (or transmittance) of the coloured light by these solutions is recorded. A calibration graph such as that below is drawn.

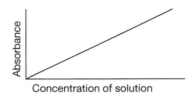

A sample of the solution whose concentration is unknown is then placed in the colorimeter and its absorbance is measured. The concentration can then be read off from the calibration graph.

In this particular experiment, the amount of manganese in a piece of steel is measured by the following method.

1. The steel is weighed and dissolved in nitric acid. This oxidises the metals present to metal ions.

2. A strong oxidising agent is added to oxidise all the Mn^{2+} ions to purple MnO_4^-.

3. All the solution is washed into a standard flask and made up to the graduation mark.

4. A sample of this solution is placed in the colorimeter (or spectrophotometer) and its absorbance measured. The concentration of permanganate is then read off the calibration graph.

5. From the concentration and the volume of the diluted solution, the number of moles of permanganate (and therefore manganese) ions can be calculated. This is converted to a mass of manganese which can be expressed as a percentage of the mass of the original steel sample.

PROBLEM

A steel nail weighing 0.847 g was analysed to estimate the percentage of manganese present. The nail was first dissolved in acid to convert all the manganese to Mn^{2+} ions. The solution was then treated with a strong oxidising agent to convert the Mn^{2+} ions to permanganate ions, MnO_4^-. The entire solution was made up to 100 cm^3 in a standard flask using distilled water.

Known concentrations of potassium permanganate solution were made up and their absorbances measured in a colorimeter using a green filter. The calibration graph below was obtained.

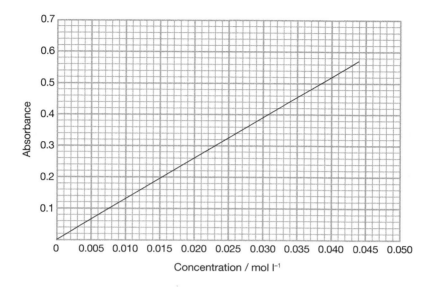

A sample of the permanganate solution obtained from treating the nail was analysed in the colorimeter and found to have an absorbance of 0.44.

(a) Write the ion–electron equation for the oxidation of the manganese metal to manganese(II) ions.

(b) Write the ion–electron equation for the oxidation of manganese(II) ions to permanganate ions. (Refer to page 11 of the Data Book.)

(c) From the calibration graph obtain the concentration of the permanganate solution.

(d) Calculate the mass of manganese in the nail.

(e) Calculate the percentage, by mass, of manganese in the nail.

Compleximetric Determination of Nickel using EDTA

EDTA, short for ethylenediaminetetraacetic acid, forms complexes with metal ions on a 1 mole : 1 mole basis. The EDTA ion has six lone pairs of electrons which act as ligands, surrounding the metal ion in an octahedral structure. Neither the formula for EDTA nor the detailed structure of the complex needs to be known.

A known concentration of EDTA solution can be titrated against an unknown concentration of a metal ion, using an indicator specific for the particular metal ion involved. In the example considered here, the ion is Ni^{2+} and the indicator is called murexide. The concentration of the metal ion can then be calculated in exactly the same way as an unknown concentration of acid can be calculated after a titration with a known concentration of alkali. A simplified equation for the complexing reaction is given below.

$$Ni^{2+}(aq) + EDTA^{2-}(aq) \rightarrow Ni\text{-}EDTA(aq)$$

PROBLEM

2.79 g of an unknown nickel(II) salt was weighed out and made up to 100 cm³ of solution in a standard flask. Then 25 cm³ portions of this solution were titrated with standard 0.10 mol l⁻¹ EDTA solution with murexide as an indicator. The average titre to reach the endpoint was 29.35 cm³ of EDTA.

(a) Calculate:

    (i)   the number of moles of Ni^{2+} in a 25 cm³ sample;

    (ii) the number of moles of Ni^{2+} in the 100 cm³ solution, i.e. in the original sample;

    (iii) the total mass of Ni^{2+} in the original sample;

    (iv) the percentage mass of Ni^{2+} in the original sample.

(b) Identify the unknown sample from the following nickel(II) salts:

    (i) $Ni(NO_3)_2.6H_2O$ (ii) $Ni(SO_4).6H_2O$ (iii) $NiCl_2.6H_2O$

Gravimetric Determination of Water in Hydrated Barium Chloride

Barium chloride is one of many salts which can exist in a hydrated form, where a specific number of molecules of water are associated with each formula of the actual salt. Hydrated barium chloride has the formula $BaCl_2.2H_2O$, meaning that for every $BaCl_2$ there are two water molecules in the crystal. These water molecules can be easily removed by strong heating to give the anhydrous (without water) salt.

In this experiment, a known mass of hydrated barium chloride is heated to constant mass, i.e. until it does not get any lighter even after more heating. The number of moles of the anhydrous salt and the number of moles of the water which have been lost are calculated and the number of water molecules per mole of $BaCl_2$ obtained, giving the value $2H_2O$ for every $BaCl_2$: i.e. the formula of the hydrated compound is $BaCl_2.2H_2O$. This type of analysis, where measurement of mass is involved, is known as gravimetric, meaning 'measuring weight'. (See Chapter 5 in Part One of this book).

PROBLEM

2.68 g of hydrated barium chloride was heated until constant mass. The remaining anhydrous salt weighed 2.26 g.

Calculate:

(a) the number of moles of $BaCl_2$ (i.e. the anhydrous salt);

(b) the number of moles of water in the hydrated sample;

(c) the number of moles of water present for each mole of $BaCl_2$.

Aqueous potassium iodide solution and cyclohexane are two examples of immiscible liquids (i.e. they don't mix). When iodine solution is shaken up with these liquids, some of the iodine dissolves in one layer and the rest dissolves in the other. An equilibrium is set up which can be described as below:

$$I_2(aq) \rightleftharpoons I_2(cyclohexane)$$

The equilibrium constant for this process is called the **partition coefficient**. It can be calculated by measuring the concentration of the iodine in each layer separately. This is done by titrating the iodine with standard sodium thiosulphate solution, $Na_2S_2O_3$. The reactions taking place are:

$$2S_2O_3^{2-}(aq) \rightarrow S_4O_6^{2-}(aq) + 2e^-$$

$$I_2(aq) + 2e^- \rightarrow 2I^-(aq)$$

Starch is used as an indicator; as long as I_2 remains, it will form a blue-black colour with starch. At the endpoint, one drop of thiosulphate will cause the colour to disappear completely.

PROBLEM

Iodine is shaken up in aqueous potassium iodide solution and cyclohexane, both immiscible. A 25 cm³ sample of each layer is titrated with standard 0.05 mol l⁻¹ sodium thiosulphate solution. The aqueous layer required 10 cm³ of thiosulphate solution to reach endpoint with the iodine; the cyclohexane layer required 15 cm³. Calculate:

(a) the concentration of iodine in each layer;

(b) the partition coefficient for the equilibrium:

$$I_2(aq) \rightleftharpoons I_2(cyclohexane)$$

Verification of a Thermodynamic Prediction

Sodium hydrogencarbonate decomposes with heat to form sodium carbonate, steam and carbon dioxide according to the equation below:

$$2NaHCO_3(s) \rightarrow Na_2CO_3(s) + H_2O(g) + CO_2(g)$$

The temperature at which decomposition takes place spontaneously can be obtained from the thermodynamic information below by calculating $\Delta H°_f$ and $\Delta S°$ for the overall reaction, and then obtaining the value for T which makes $\Delta G° = 0$ in the equation $\Delta G° = \Delta H° - T\Delta S$. (See Chapter 12 in Part One of this book.)

Compound	$\Delta H°_f$ / kJ mol^{-1}	$S°$ / J mol^{-1} K^{-1}
$NaHCO_3(s)$	−951	102
$Na_2CO_3(s)$	−1131	135
$H_2O(g)$	−242	189
CO_2	−394	214

PROBLEM 1

(a) Calculate $\Delta H°$ and $\Delta S°$ for the above reaction, per mole of equation as written.

(b) Calculate the temperature at which the decomposition of sodium hydrogencarbonate becomes spontaneous.

The temperature at which decomposition takes place spontaneously can be obtained experimentally using the apparatus shown.

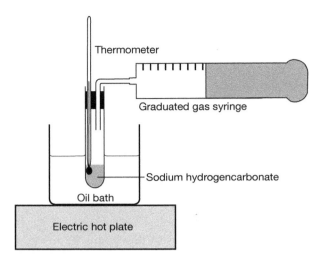

The oil acts as a 'bath' which heats the sodium hydrogencarbonate in the test tube slowly and evenly. The oil should be stirred so that the heat is evenly applied to the compound to prevent some parts of it being hotter than others. It important to heat the compound slowly since we want to record the volume of carbon dioxide gas given off at measured temperatures. The gas will take time to come off and push the syringe out; heating too quickly would mean that the recorded temperature would be higher than that at which the measured gas volume had been obtained.

A graph of gas volume against temperature can then be drawn. Such a graph is shown below.

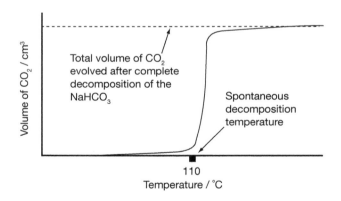

As can be seen, little carbon dioxide is given off until approximately 110 °C (383K), when there is a large increase in the volume of gas being produced over a small range above that temperature.

PROBLEM 2

Calculate the mass of sodium hydrogencarbonate which would decompose completely to give 90.0 cm³ of carbon dioxide. Assume the molar volume of carbon dioxide at room temperature to be 24 litres mol⁻¹.

Kinetics of the Acid-Catalysed Propanone/Iodine Reaction

Propanone and iodine react according to the following equation:

$$CH_3COCH_3(aq) + I_2(aq) + H^+(aq) \rightarrow CH_3COCH_2I(aq) + HI(aq)$$

The reaction is first order with respect to propanone and first order with respect to the hydrogen ions which catalyse the reaction.

The order with respect to iodine can be determined by carrying out the reaction with much higher concentrations of propanone and hydrogen ions than the iodine concentration. In this situation, the iodine concentration will drop significantly as the reaction proceeds, but the changes in the propanone and hydrogen ion concentrations will be very slight in comparison. We can therefore regard the concentrations of propanone and hydrogen ion as being approximately constant during the experiment.

A solution of iodine and a solution of propanone mixed with acid are made up. They are then mixed together and a stopclock started. Every few minutes, a sample of the reaction mixture is dropped by pipette into a flask containing sodium carbonate solution and the contents titrated with sodium thiosulphate solution. The purpose of the sodium carbonate solution is to 'stop' the reaction by diluting the reactants and by neutralising the acid catalyst.

This titration is based on the reaction come across in PPA 5 (Determination of a Partition Coefficient), but the details are repeated here.

The thiosulphate reacts with iodine according to the ion-electron equations:

$$2S_2O_3^{2-}(aq) \rightarrow S_4O_6^{2-}(aq) + 2e^-$$
$$I_2(aq) + 2e^- \rightarrow 2I^-(aq)$$

Starch is used as an indicator; as long as I_2 remains, it will form a blue-black colour with starch. At the endpoint, one drop of thiosulphate solution will cause the colour to disappear completely.

The concentration of iodine in each sample (which is the concentration of the iodine in the reaction mixture) can be calculated at each time, knowing the concentration of the sodium thiosulphate solution. A graph of concentration of iodine against time can then be plotted. A typical result is shown.

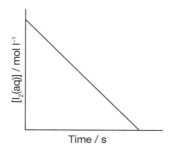

This graph shows that the rate of reaction, measured by the gradient of the graph, is constant. That is, the rate of decrease of iodine is *not* affected by the decreasing concentration of iodine as the reaction proceeds. *The order of reaction with respect to iodine is therefore zero.*

We can now write the rate equation because we are told that the reaction is first order with respect to both hydrogen ions and propanone and we have shown experimentally that it is zero order with respect to iodine. So

$$\text{rate} = k[\text{H}^+(\text{aq})][\text{CH}_3\text{COCH}_3(\text{aq})]$$

The rate constant for the reaction, k, can be calculated using this equation and the information below.

- The rate of reaction is the gradient of the graph, in units of mol l^{-1} s^{-1}.

- The concentrations of hydrogen ion and propanone are known at the start of the experiment and are assumed to be constant in comparison to the quickly decreasing concentration of iodine.

PROBLEM

A mixture of propanone and sulphuric acid is added to a solution of iodine and a timer is started. At intervals, samples of the reaction mixture are titrated with sodium thiosulphate solution to measure the iodine concentration. The initial concentration of sulphuric acid in the reaction mixture is 0.050 mol l^{-1}; that of the propanone is 2.00 mol l^{-1}. A graph of concentration of iodine against time is plotted; this is shown overleaf.

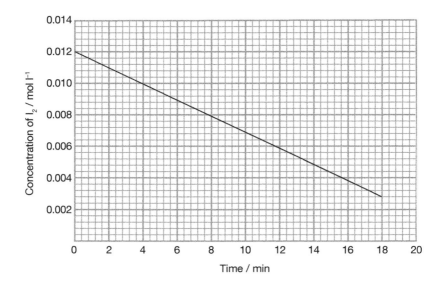

(a) Calculate the rate of reaction, in mol l⁻¹ s⁻¹, from the graph. (Note that the time axis on the graph has *minutes* as the unit.)

(b) Using the information given about the initial concentrations of propanone and sulphuric acid in the reaction mixture, calculate the rate constant, k, for the reaction, giving the correct unit. Note: Sulphuric acid, H_2SO_4, is **diprotic**, i.e. it produces two H^+ ions for every H_2SO_4.

Cyclohexene (a cyclic alkene) can be obtained from cyclohexanol (a cyclic alcohol) by **dehydration** using a **dehydrating agent** such as concentrated phosphoric acid or sulphuric acid. The process can be represented by the equation below.

Note that the hexagon is a short way of representing a cyclohexane ring. Each corner represents a carbon and two hydrogens unless some other group, e.g. the –O–H, is shown, as in the cyclohexanol, or unless a C=C double bond is shown, as in the cyclohexene. Note that this hexagon is *not* the same as a benzene ring which is shown as

and which has the formula C_6H_6.

The reaction is carried out by heating the cyclohexanol and concentrated phosphoric (or sulphuric) acid. After heating for some time, the cyclohexene formed is distilled off at its boiling point and collected.

The percentage yield can be calculated by working out what mass of product would have been obtained had all the original known mass of cyclohexanol reacted and then expressing the actual mass of product as a percentage of this.

PROBLEM

6.23 g of cyclohexanol is reacted with concentrated phosphoric acid, and the cyclohexene product is distilled off. 3.31 g of product is obtained. Express this as a percentage yield.

Identification by Derivative Formation

It is often the case in organic chemistry that an unknown compound can be identified by *type*, e.g. alcohol, aldehyde, ketone, etc., by simple chemical tests, but determining the *exact* compound can be difficult. The boiling point and melting point of an unknown compound can be helpful, but if any impurity is present this will affect the readings to such a large extent as to make them useless for proper identification.

What can be very useful is to make a solid **derivative** of the compound – a new substance **derived from** (made from) the original. If this new substance can be obtained and purified by **recrystallisation,** a melting point can then be taken which, with reference to data tables, can identify the original unknown.

A particularly useful compound for making a derivative of an aldehyde or ketone is **2, 4 dinitrophenylhydrazine**. It can react with a carbonyl compound as shown.

The 2,4 dinitrophenylhydrazone product (note that the derivative is now a hydra**zone**) has a melting point which is unique for the particular carbonyl compound involved.

Neither the structural formula of the hydrazine nor the hydrazone needs to be remembered fully, but you should be able to recognise them. (The **dinitrophenyl** part of the name, referring to the **two NO$_2$** (**nitro**) groups joined to a **phenyl** group, should be easy to spot.) The overall process, represented by the equation above, is a **condensation** because the two molecules are joining and water is released.

An important aspect of making a derivative for identification is the process of recrystallisation, which enables a very pure sample of the derivative to be obtained. If the sample is *not* pure, its melting point is substantially reduced, making accurate identification impossible.

Recrystallisation is based on the fact that the derivative is *soluble in hot solvent* (in this case ethanol), but *insoluble in cold solvent*. The procedure is as follows:

1.   The impure derivative is dissolved in hot ethanol. Both the derivative and the impurities dissolve.

2.   The solution is allowed to cool. Since the derivative does not dissolve in cold ethanol, it precipitates out as solid crystals. Most of the impurities remain in solution.

3.   The solid derivative is filtered and kept; the solvent, containing impurities, is discarded.

If the crystals of the derivative are sharp and well formed, that is a good indication that the sample is pure. If the crystals are less well formed, this indicates that there are still impurities present. The entire process of steps 1 to 3 can then be repeated, if necessary several times, until good crystals are obtained. The more often the process is repeated, the less yield of product there will be, because there is inevitable loss during the purification. However, yield is not important; obtaining a very pure sample for accurate identification is. The sample is then dried in an oven (at a temperature well below the expected melting point).

The melting point of the compound is then taken by putting a small sample into a thin glass tube, sealed at the bottom end, and placing it into a melting point apparatus. The melting point apparatus is a metal block in the centre of which there are small holes for inserting samples to be tested. A further hole, close to the tubes, contains a thermometer. The metal block is heated electrically and the sample is observed, usually with the aid of a built-in magnifying glass. When the sample is seen to melt, the temperature is read.

An important point of the procedure is to slow the rate of heating down as the melting point is approached. This is because the heat gets to the sample quickly, since the tube is thin; the heat going to the liquid in the thermometer takes longer because it is thicker. It also takes time for the thermometer liquid to expand and reach the level at which the temperature can be read accurately. This is known as **thermal inertia**. (Inertia means sluggishness or unwillingness to move.) If heating was fast, the sample could be seen melting but the heat has not yet had time to cause the thermometer liquid to get to the level where it is reading the correct temperature. The reading taken would therefore be inaccurate.

Preparation of Benzoic Acid by Hydrolysis of Ethyl Benzoate

Benzoic acid can be prepared by hydrolysing the ester ethyl benzoate using alkali. This is done by **refluxing** a mixture of the ester and the alkali. Refluxing involves heating the mixture in a flask fitted with a vertical condenser. This is a tube contained within an outer jacket through which cold water flows. It enables the vapours of the boiling ester to turn back into liquid which drips back into the reaction mixture, instead of escaping into the air. This means that the heating can be carried out for quite a long time without the ester being lost, and results in more of the product being made. A diagram of this apparatus is shown below.

The original ester does not mix with aqueous solution and so appears as an oily layer on top of the alkali solution. As the boiling takes place, the layers are continuously being mixed and the reaction between the ester and the alkali starts to takes place. As this happens, the oily layer gradually disappears; the reaction has gone to completion when the oily ester layer has gone completely. The contents of the flask are now the soluble products. These products are **sodium benzoate** and **ethanol**. The equation for the reaction is shown below:

Once the solution of sodium benzoate and ethanol has cooled, hydrochloric acid is added. This has the effect of precipitating out solid crystals of benzoic acid. The equation for this is shown below.

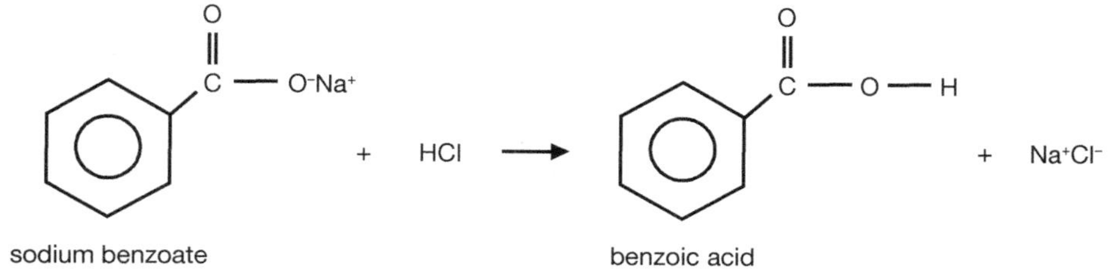

sodium benzoate   benzoic acid

This reaction takes place because benzoic acid is a **weak acid**. The benzoate ion therefore 'prefers' to join with the hydrogen ion from hydrochloric acid, to form benzoic acid, rather than being free in solution. The equilibrium for the dissociation of benzoic acid, shown by the equation below, is mainly to the left; that is, benzoic acid only dissociates to a small extent.

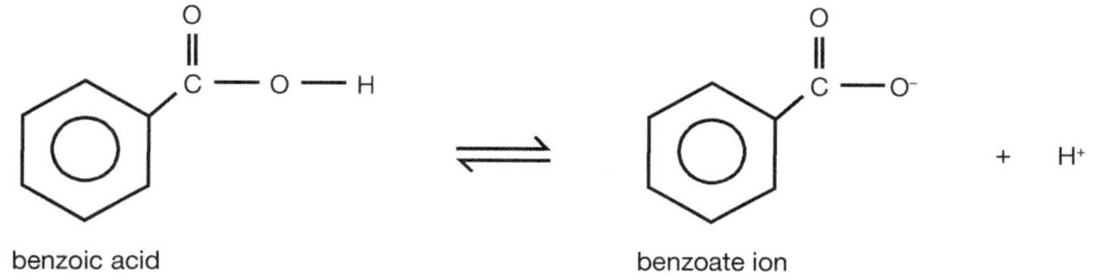

benzoic acid   benzoate ion

The crystals of benzoic acid are filtered out and recrystallised to obtain a pure sample. (See PPA 9 for an explanation of this procedure.)

The equations describing the steps of this procedure look complicated but they are summarised (in simplified form) on the following page. Hydrolysis means breaking a compound using water (although usually helped by acid or alkali). One part of the original molecule gets a hydrogen atom from the water and the other gets a hydroxyl (–O–H) group in the breaking process.

Note that the formula for ethanol has been written 'back to front', instead of the more usual CH_3CH_2OH, to show more clearly where the hydrolysis takes place.

PROBLEM

3.75 g of ethyl benzoate was refluxed with sodium hydroxide solution for 30 minutes. The resulting solution was treated with dilute hydrochloric acid, which caused benzoic acid to be precipitated. The crystals were filtered, recrystallised, dried and weighed. The mass of benzoic acid obtained was found to be 1.83 g. Express this as a percentage yield of the maximum obtainable from the original sample of ethyl benzoate.

Preparation of Aspirin

Aspirin is an ester which can be prepared by the reaction of salicylic acid and ethanoic anhydride as shown below.

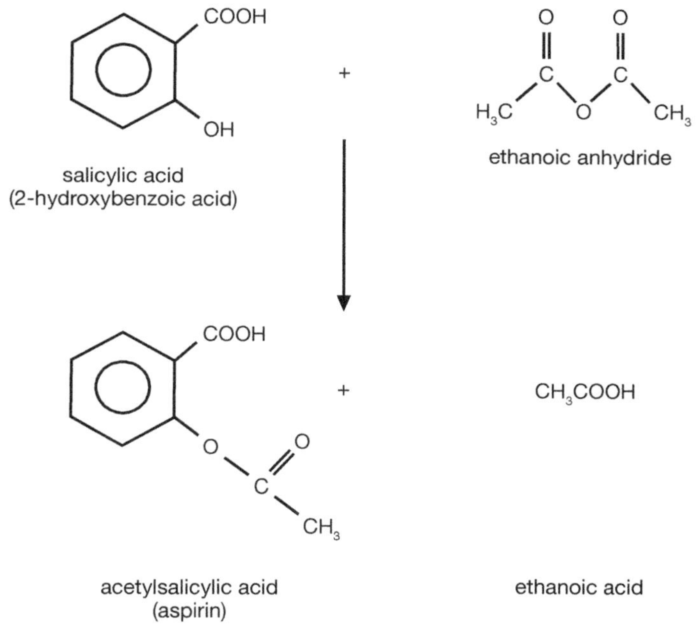

salicylic acid
(2-hydroxybenzoic acid)

ethanoic anhydride

acetylsalicylic acid
(aspirin)

ethanoic acid

The formulae and names of the unfamiliar compounds need not be learned. What should be noticed is that the above equation represents a **condensation reaction**. This term has usually referred to joining two molecules, with the release of a water molecule, although in the Organic Chemistry course the release of an HCl molecule when two molecules joined was also described as condensation. The term generally means joining two molecules with the release of a *small* molecule. In the above case, the small molecule is ethanoic acid, CH_3COOH.

Also note that aspirin is an **ester**, which has the characteristic –COO– group connecting two carbon-containing groups. Usually we have come across esters as having been formed by the reaction of an alcohol and a carboxylic acid; in this case, the ester has been made by the reaction of an alcohol group with a **derivative** of an acid, namely ethanoic anhydride.

6.90 g of salicylic acid is reacted with an excess of ethanoic anhydride to make aspirin. The mass of aspirin obtained is 6.75 g. Express this as a percentage yield of product.

Aspirin Determination

Aspirin (acetylsalicylic acid) has the formula:

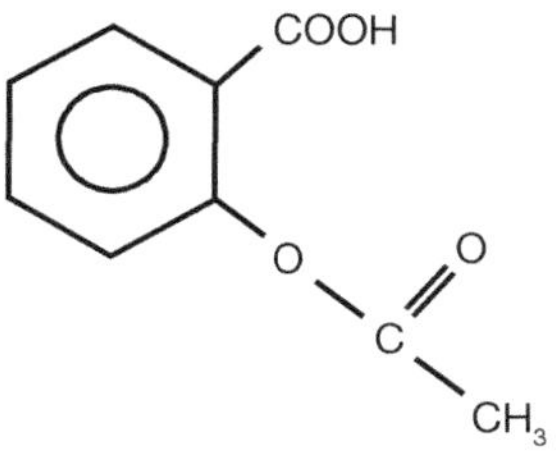

The amount of aspirin in a tablet can be determined by a technique known as 'back titration'. This is used because aspirin is insoluble in water and cannot be analysed by the more normal direct titration.

An excess of alkali is added to the tablet. This hydrolyses the aspirin into salicylic acid and ethanoic acid and then neutralises the two acids to form their sodium salts, i.e. sodium salicylate and sodium ethanoate, shown below as a single step rather than two.

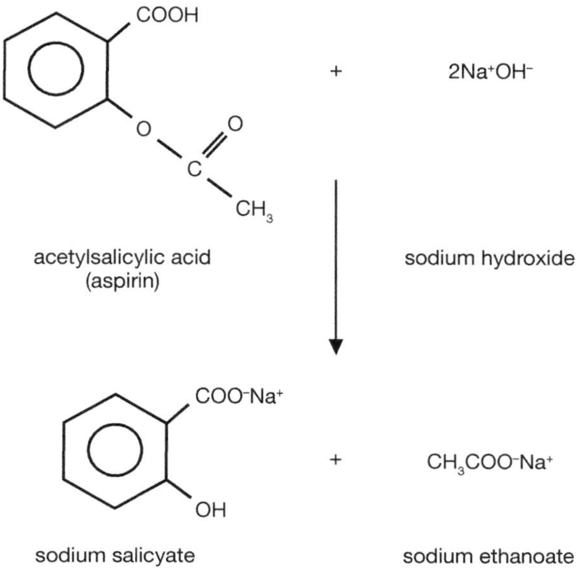

acetylsalicylic acid
(aspirin)

$+$ $2Na^+OH^-$

sodium hydroxide

sodium salicyate

$+$ $CH_3COO^-Na^+$

sodium ethanoate

The excess alkali present after neutralisation is then titrated with acid of known concentration. This gives us the number of moles of alkali remaining in solution. Knowing the number of moles of alkali originally added, the number of moles of alkali which neutralised the two acids from the aspirin can be obtained by subtraction. From this we get the number of moles of aspirin present in the orginal tablet, and therefore the mass of aspirin.

PROBLEM

A tablet of aspirin weighing 1.04 g is completely hydrolysed by 25 cm^3 of 1 mol l^{-1} NaOH solution. The resulting solution is transferred to a 250 cm^3 standard flask and made up to the mark with distilled water. Then 25 cm^3 portions of this solution are titrated with 0.10 mol l^{-1} hydrochloric acid. The average titre is 15.9 cm^3 of acid.

Calculate:

(a) the number of moles of NaOH solution added to the tablet;

(b) the number of moles of HCl needed to neutralise the excess NaOH solution present in a 25 cm^3 sample of the solution in the standard flask;

(c) the number of moles of NaOH present in each 25 cm^3 sample from the solution in the standard flask;

(d) the number of moles of NaOH present in the 250 cm^3 standard flask when the solution was made up (this is the number of moles of NaOH in excess, i.e. the number of moles of NaOH left over after the tablet had been hydrolysed and neutralized);

(e) the number of moles of NaOH which had neutralised and hydrolysed the aspirin;

(f) the number of moles of aspirin in the tablet (note that 1 mole of aspirin reacts with 2 moles of NaOH);

(g) the mass of aspirin present in the tablet (1 mole of aspirin = 180 g);

(h) the percentage of aspirin in the tablet (1 mole of aspirin = 180 g).

Answers

Answers

CHAPTER 1 – Electromagnetic Spectrum

1 170 kJ mol^{-1}
2 (a) 554 nm   (b) 216 kJ mol^{-1}
3 302 kJ mol^{-1}
4 (a) 650 nm   (b) 184 kJ mol^{-1}
5 (a) 588 nm   (b) 204 kJ mol^{-1}

6 620 nm
7 389 nm
8 405 nm
9 487 nm
10 325 nm

CHAPTER 2 – Volumetric Analysis

1 0.670 mol l^{-1}
2 0.184 mol l^{-1}
3 (a) 14.2 cm^3 (b) 0.142 mol l^{-1}
4 (a) 2.89 g   (b) 79.4%
5 (a) 0.0917 mol l^{-1} (b) 0.409 mol l^{-1}

6 0.249 mol l^{-1}
7 1.57 mol l^{-1}
8 0.126 mol l^{-1}
9 0.0597 mol l^{-1}
10 (a) 3.60 g   (b) 53.6%

CHAPTER 3 – Redox Titrations

1 50 cm^3
2 16.0 cm^3
3 (a) 33.6 cm^3 (b) 0.0269 mol   (c) 2.15 mol l^{-1}
4 (a) 8.20×10^{-4} mol   (b) 4.10×10^{-3} mol   (c) 2.29 g   (d) 92.0%
5 93.6%
6 (a) 6.20×10^{-4} mol   (b) 0.620 mol l^{-1}
7 (a) 18.6 cm^3 (b) 2.23×10^{-3} mol   (c) 0.0223 mol   (d) 1.25 g
   (e) 87.1%
8 (a) 3.12×10^{-3} mol   (b) 0.0156 mol   (c) 1.25 mol l^{-1}
9 (a) 2.15×10^{-3} mol   (b) 0.0215 mol   (c) 0.859 mol l^{-1}
10 (a) 2.36×10^{-3} mol   (b) 2.76 g   (c) 8.52%

CHAPTER 4 – Empirical Formulae

1 SnO_2
2 CH_4
3 (a) NO_2 (b) N_2O_4
4 (a) CH_2 (b) $C_{10}H_{20}$
5 (a) Si_2H_5 (b) Si_4H_{10}

6 (a) CNH_4 (b) $C_2N_2H_8$
7 $Ca_3P_2O_8$
8 FeC_5O_5
9 $BaSO_3$
10 (a) C_3H_2I (b) $C_6H_4I_2$

CHAPTER 5 – Gravimetric Analysis

1 (a) 1.78 g   (b) 35.5%
2 (a) 5.02 g   (b) 79.4 %
3 (a) 0.00716 mol   (b) 1.02 g   (c) 5.33 g   (d) 84.0%
4 (a) 1.23 g   (b) 0.808%
5 (a) 5.11 g   (b) 69.6%
6 (a) 0.0125   (b) 0.025   (c) 2
7 (a) 3   (b) $Cu(NO_3)_2.3H_2O$
8 (a) 10   (b) $Na_2CO_3.10H_2O$
9 (a) 6   (b) $FeSO_4.6H_2O$
10 (a) 10   (b) $Na_2SO_4.10H_2O$
11 (a) CH_2 (b) C_5H_{10}
12 (a) C_2H_4O (b) $C_4H_8O_2$
13 $C_5H_{10}O_2$
14 $C_7H_{14}O_2$
15 $C_9H_{10}O_2$

CHAPTER 6 – The Equilibrium Constant and Partition Coefficient

1 50
2 160
3 9.6
4 8
5 0.5
6 9.6×10^{-4}
7 9
8 0.735
9 0.112
10 27
11 0.794
12 (a) Ethoxyethane layer: 0.223 mol l^{-1}; aqueous layer 0.148 mol l^{-1}
    (b) 0.664
13 (a) $[I_2](aq) = 0.0620$ mol l^{-1}; $[I_2(cyclohexane)] = 0.0930$ mol l^{-1}
    (b) 1.50
14 (a) 0.568 mol l^{-1} (b) 1.70 g
15 (a) 0.036 mol l^{-1} (b) 0.234 g

CHAPTER 7 – pH of Solutions and the Ionic Product of Water

1 0.699
2 7.20
3 4.42
4 0.439
5 −0.398
6 0.0269 mol l^{-1}
7 1.35×10^{-5} mol l^{-1}

8 1.58×10^{-10} mol l^{-1}
9 1.26×10^{-13} mol l^{-1}
10 1.42 mol l^{-1}
11 (a) 5.01×10^{-13} mol l^{-1} (b) 0.0200 mol l^{-1}
12 (a) 0.0348 mol l^{-1} (b) 1.46
13 (a) 1.57×10^{-14} mol l^{-1} (b) 13.8
14 (a) 1.79 mol l^{-1} (b) 5.58×10^{-15} mol l^{-1}
15 (a) 3.31×10^{-4} mol l^{-1} (b) 3.02×10^{-11} mol l^{-1}

CHAPTER 8 – Dissociation Constants and the pH of Weak Acids

1 1.34×10^{-3} mol l^{-1} **11** 0.0513 mol l^{-1}
2 0.200 mol l^{-1} **12** 0.0871 mol l^{-1}
3 7.21×10^{-4} mol l^{-1} **13** 0.0537 mol l^{-1}
4 0.498 mol l^{-1} **14** 2.57×10^{-4} mol l^{-1}
5 1.47×10^{-5} mol l^{-1} **15** 6.31×10^{-3} mol l^{-1}
6 2.88 **16** 3.70
7 2.22 **17** 1.86
8 1.74 **18** 4.12
9 2.51 **19** 3.04
10 2.72 **20** 4.84

CHAPTER 9 – Buffer Solutions

1 5.16
2 4.43
3 4.80
4 4.87
5 4.15
6 4.46
7 3.87
8 3.60
9 5.17
10 4.46
11 Acid : salt ratio = 2.14 or salt : acid ratio = 0.468
12 Acid : salt ratio = 0.398 or salt : acid ratio = 2.51
13 Acid : salt ratio = 0.275 or salt : acid ratio = 3.63
14 Acid : salt ratio = 3.55 or salt : acid ratio = 0.282
15 Acid : salt ratio = 2.29 or salt : acid ratio = 0.437

CHAPTER 10 – Using Bond Enthalpies

1	-631 kJ mol^{-1}	**6**	-291 kJ mol^{-1}
2	-778 kJ mol^{-1}	**7**	-221 kJ mol^{-1}
3	-97 kJ mol^{-1}	**8**	320 kJ mol^{-1}
4	-561 kJ mol^{-1}	**9**	338 kJ mol^{-1}
5	-58 kJ mol^{-1}	**10**	-66 kJ mol^{-1}

CHAPTER 11 – Enthalpy Diagrams (Born–Haber Cycles)

1 -416 kJ mol^{-1}.

2 (a) $\Delta H_1 = 159$ kJ mol^{-1}; $\Delta H_2 = 78$ kJ mol^{-1} (using the enthalpy of atomisation of F), or 77.5 kJ mol^{-1} (using $\frac{1}{2}$ the bond enthalpy of F–F); $\Delta H_3 = 526$ kJ mol^{-1}; $\Delta H_4 = -328$ kJ mol^{-1}; $\Delta H_5 = -1030$ kJ mol^{-1}

    (b) -595 kJ mol^{-1} (or -595.5 kJ mol^{-1} if $\frac{1}{2}$ the bond enthalpy of F–F, 77.5 kJ mol^{-1}, had been used instead of the enthalpy of atomisation of F)

3 (a) $\Delta H_1 = 81$ kJ mol^{-1}; $\Delta H_2 = 78$ kJ mol^{-1} (or 77.5 kJ mol^{-1}; see answer to Question 2 for explanation); $\Delta H_3 = 409$ kJ mol^{-1}; $\Delta H_4 = -328$ kJ mol^{-1}

    (b) -775 kJ mol^{-1} (or -774.5 kJ mol^{-1})

4 (a) $\Delta H_1 = 147$ kJ mol^{-1}; $\Delta H_2 = 243$ kJ mol^{-1} if the bond enthalpy of Cl–Cl has been used; 242 kJ mol^{-1} if the enthalpy of atomisation of Cl has been used); $\Delta H_3 = 744$ kJ mol^{-1}; $\Delta H_4 = 1460$ kJ mol^{-1}; $\Delta H_5 = -698$ kJ mol^{-1}; $\Delta H_6 = -2326$ kJ mol l^{-1}

    (b) -430 kJ mol^{-1} if the bond enthalpy of Cl–Cl has been used; or -431 kJ mol^{-1} if the enthalpy of atomisation of Cl has been used

5 (a) $\Delta H_1 = 430$ kJ mol^{-1}; $\Delta H_2 = 155$ kJ mol^{-1} if the Bond Enthalpy of F–F has been used; 156 kJ mol^{-1} if $2 \times$ the enthalpy of atomisation of F has been used; $\Delta H_3 = 743$ kJ mol^{-1}; $\Delta H_4 = 1770$ kJ mol^{-1}; $\Delta H_5 = -656$ kJ mol^{-1}; $\Delta H_6 = -2845$ kJ mol l^{-1}

    (b) -403 kJ mol^{-1} if the bond enthalpy of F–F has been used; or -402 kJ mol^{-1} if the enthalpy of atomisation of F has been used

6 (a) $\Delta H_1 = 671$ kJ mol^{-1}; $\Delta H_2 = -321$ kJ mol^{-1}; $\Delta H_3 = -337$ kJ mol^{-1}

    (b) 13 kJ mol^{-1}

7 (a) $\Delta H_1 = 732$ kJ mol^{-1}; $\Delta H_2 = -405$ kJ mol^{-1}; $\Delta H_3 = -337$ kJ mol^{-1}

    (b) -10 kJ mol^{-1}

8 (a) $\Delta H_1 = 834$ kJ mol^{-1}; $\Delta H_2 = -520$ kJ mol^{-1}; $\Delta H_3 = -364$ kJ mol^{-1}

    (b) -50 kJ mol^{-1}

9 (a) $\Delta H_1 = 2913$ kJ mol^{-1}; $\Delta H_2 = -1920$ kJ mol^{-1}; $\Delta H_3 = -1012$ kJ mol^{-1}

    (b) -19 kJ mol^{-1}

10 (a) $\Delta H_1 = 2127$ kJ mol^{-1}; $\Delta H_2 = -1480$ kJ mol^{-1}; $\Delta H_3 = -728$ kJ mol^{-1}

    (b) -81 kJ mol^{-1}

CHAPTER 12 – $\Delta H°$, $\Delta S°$ and $\Delta G°$

1 (a) $\Delta H° = 271$ kJ mol^{-1}; $\Delta S° = 172$ J K^{-1} mol^{-1} or 0.172 kJ K^{-1} mol^{-1}
   (b) 219 kJ mol^{-1}
   (c) Above 1580 K

2 (a) $\Delta H° = 166$ kJ mol^{-1}; $\Delta S° = 476$ J K^{-1} mol^{-1} or 0.476 kJ K^{-1} mol^{-1}
   (b) -72 kJ mol^{-1}
   (c) Above 349 K

3 (a) $\Delta H° = 176$ kJ mol^{-1}; $\Delta S° = 285$ J K^{-1} mol^{-1} or 0.285 kJ K^{-1} mol^{-1}
   (b) -109 kJ mol^{-1}
   (c) Above 618 K

4 (a) $\Delta H° = -92$ kJ mol^{-1}; $\Delta S° = -199$ J K^{-1} mol^{-1} or -0.199 kJ K^{-1} mol^{-1}
   (b) 7.50 kJ mol^{-1}
   (c) Below 462 K

5 (a) $\Delta H° = -882$ kJ mol^{-1}; $\Delta S° = -147$ J K^{-1} mol^{-1} or -0.147 kJ K^{-1} mol^{-1}
   (b) -794 kJ mol^{-1}
   (c) Below 6000 K

6 (a) $\Delta H° = 135$ kJ mol^{-1}; $\Delta S° = 334$ J K^{-1} mol^{-1} or 0.334 kJ K^{-1} mol^{-1}
   (b) -65.4 kJ mol^{-1}
   (c) Above 404 K

7 (a) $\Delta H° = -99$ kJ mol^{-1}; $\Delta S° = -93.5$ J K^{-1} mol^{-1} or -0.0935 kJ K^{-1} mol^{-1}
   (b) -71.1 kJ mol $^{-1}$
   (c) Below 1060 K

8 (a) $\Delta H° = -200$ kJ mol^{-1}; $\Delta S° = -195$ J K^{-1} mol^{-1} or -0.195 kJ K^{-1} mol^{-1}
   (b) -258.5 kJ mol^{-1}
   (c) Below 1030 K

9 (a) $\Delta H° = -209$ kJ mol^{-1}; $\Delta S° = -367$ J mol^{-1} K^{-1} or -0.367 kJ mol^{-1} K^{-1}
   (b) Below 569 K

10 (a) $\Delta H° = 104$ kJ mol^{-1}; $\Delta S° = 7.00$ J K^{-1} mol^{-1} or 7.00×10^{-3} kJ K^{-1} mol^{-1}
   (b) 102 kJ K^{-1} mol^{-1}
   (c) Above 1.49×10^4 K

CHAPTER 13 – Electrochemical Cells

1 (a) $Mg(s) \rightarrow Mg^{2+}(aq) + 2e^-$ and $Pb^{2+}(aq) + 2e^- \rightarrow Pb(s)$
   (b) $Mg(s) + Pb^{2+}(aq) \rightarrow Mg^{2+}(aq) + Pb(s)$
   (c) 2.24 V
   (d) 432 kJ mol^{-1}

2 (a) $Ni(s) \rightarrow Ni^{2+}(aq) + 2e^-$ and $Sn^{2+}(aq) + 2e^- \rightarrow Sn(s)$
   (b) $Ni(s) + Sn^{2+}(aq) \rightarrow Ni^{2+}(aq) + Sn(s)$
   (c) 0.09 V
   (d) -17.4 kJ mol^{-1}

3 (a) $Ni(s) \rightarrow Ni^{2+}(aq) + 2e^-$ and $Ag^+(aq) + e^- \rightarrow Ag(s)$
   (b) $Ni(s) + 2Ag^+(aq) \rightarrow Ni^{2+}(aq) + 2Ag(s)$
   (c) 1.03 V
   (d) -199 kJ mol^{-1}

4 (a) 1.5 V
   (b) 289.5 kJ mol^{-1}
5 (a) $H_2O_2(aq) + 2Fe^{2+}(aq) + 2H^+(aq) \rightarrow 2H_2O(l) + 2Fe^{3+}(aq)$
   (b) 1.00 V
   (c) −193 kJ mol^{-1}
6 (a) $Br_2(l) + 2e^- \rightarrow 2Br^-(aq)$ and $SO_3^{2-}(aq) + H_2O(l) \rightarrow SO_4^{2-}(aq) + 2H^+(aq) + 2e^-$
   (b) $Br_2(l) + SO_3^{2-}(aq) + H_2O(l) \rightarrow 2Br^-(aq) + SO_4^{2-}(aq) + 2H^+(aq)$
   (c) 0.90 V
   (d) −174 kJ mol^{-1}
7 (a) −0.74 V
   (b) Cr
   (c) $3Mg(s) + 2Cr^{3+}(aq) \rightarrow 3Mg^{2+}(aq) + 2Cr(s)$
   (d) −944 kJ mol^{-1}
8 (a) 2.05 V
   (b) −396 kJ mol^{-1}
9 (a) $O_2(g) + 2H_2O(l) + 4e^- \rightarrow 4OH^-(aq)$ and $H_2(g) + 2OH^-(aq) \rightarrow 2H_2O(l) + 2e^-$
   (b) $2H_2(g) + O_2(g) \rightarrow 2H_2O(l)$
   (c) 1.23 V
   (d) −237 kJ mol^{-1}
10 (a) 0.46 V
   (b) −88.8 kJ mol^{-1}
   (c) −108 J K^{-1} mol^{-1} (or −0.108 kJ mol^{-1})

CHAPTER 14 – Rate Equations

1 (a) rate = $k[A]$ (b) 0.1 s^{-1}
2 (a) rate = $k[X][Y]$ (b) 0.2 mol^{-1} l min^{-1}
3 (a) rate = $k[B]^2$ (b) 2 mol^{-1} l s^{-1}
4 (a) rate = $k[X]^2[Y]$ (b) 0.5 mol^{-2} l^2 min^{-1}
5 (a) rate = $k[Y]^2[Z]$ (b) 2 mol^{-2} l^2 min^{-1}
6 (a) rate = $k[X][Y]$ (b) 8 mol^{-1} l s^{-1}
7 (a) rate = $k[A][C]$ (b) 20 mol^{-1} l min^{-1}
8 (a) rate = $k[Y]^2[Z]$ (b) 150 mol^{-2} l^2 min^{-1}
9 (a) rate = $k[X][Z]$ (b) 0.375 mol^{-1} l s^{-1}
10 (a) rate = $k[B]^2$ (b) 48 mol^{-1} l s^{-1}

PRESCRIBED PRACTICAL ACTIVITIES

PPA 1
90.2%

PPA 2
(a) $Mn(s) \rightarrow Mn^{2+}(aq) + 2e^-$
(b) $Mn^{2+}(aq) + 4H_2O(l) \rightarrow MnO_4^-(aq) + 8H^+(aq) + 5e^-$
(c) 0.034 mol l^{-1}
(d) 0.187 g
(e) 22.1%

PPA 3
(a) (i) 2.935×10^{-3} mol
    (ii) 0.0117 mol
    (iii) 0.689 g
    (iv) 24.7%
(b) (iii) $NiCl_2.6H_2O$

PPA 4
(a) 0.0108 mol
(b) 0.0233 mol
(c) 2 (to the nearest whole number)

PPA 5
(a) Aqueous layer = 0.01 mol l^{-1};
     cyclohexane layer = 0.015 mol l^{-1}
(b) 1.5

Note that the calculation of the partition coefficient did not need the actual concentrations of the iodine in the two layers. Since the same volume of each layer had been titrated with the same thiosulphate solution, the ratio of the volumes of the titres (15/10) gives the partition coefficient for the equilibrium described by the equation given.

PPA 6
Problem 1
(a) $\Delta H° = 135$ kJ mol^{-1};
     $\Delta S° = 334$ J K^{-1} mol l^{-1} (or
     0.334 J K^{-1} mol^{-1})
(b) Above 404 K
Problem 2
0.630 g

PPA 7
(a) 8.33×10^{-6} mol l^{-1} s^{-1}
(b) 4.17×10^{-5} mol^{-1} l s^{-1}

PPA 8
64.8%

PPA 10
60.0%

PPA 11
75%

PPA 12
(a) 0.025 mol
(b) 1.59×10^{-3} mol
(c) 1.59×10^{-3} mol
(d) 0.0159 mol
(e) 9.10×10^{-3} mol
(f) 4.55×10^{-3} mol
(g) 0.819 g
(h) 78.75%